The Open University

M208 Pure Mathematics

# AB1

# Limits

This publication forms part of an Open University course. Details of this and other Open University courses can be obtained from the Student Registration and Enquiry Service, The Open University, PO Box 197, Milton Keynes, MK7 6BJ, United Kingdom: tel. +44 (0)870 300 6090, e-mail general-enquiries@open.ac.uk

Alternatively, you may visit the Open University website at http://www.open.ac.uk where you can learn more about the wide range of courses and packs offered at all levels by The Open University.

To purchase a selection of Open University course materials, visit http://www.ouw.co.uk, or contact Open University Worldwide, Michael Young Building, Walton Hall, Milton Keynes, MK7 6AA, United Kingdom, for a brochure: tel. +44 (0)1908 858793, fax +44 (0)1908 858787, e-mail ouw-customer-services@open.ac.uk

The Open University, Walton Hall, Milton Keynes, MK7 6AA.

First published 2006. Reprinted with amendments 2007.



Edited, designed and typeset by The Open University, using the Open University TEX System.

Printed and bound in the United Kingdom by Hobbs the Printers Limited, Brunel Road, Totton, Hampshire SO40 3WX.

ISBN 0 7492 0211 4

1.2

# Contents

# Introduction to Analysis Block B

In Analysis Block B we continue the process of putting the foundations of calculus on a firm logical basis. At the end of Analysis Block A we met the idea of a continuous function, and at the start of Analysis Block B we introduce the related ideas of a *limit* of a function and of *uniform continuity*. Then we use these ideas to study *differentiation* and *integration* in detail. Finally, we discuss the representation of functions by *power series*.

You will meet many applications of these ideas, including:

- a technique for proving inequalities such as
$$\log_e(1+x) > x - \tfrac{1}{2}x^2, \quad \text{for } x \in (0,\infty);$$
- a strange function which is continuous but nowhere differentiable;
- Stirling's approximate formula for $n!$;
- several remarkable exact formulas for $\pi$, including Wallis' Product,
$$\frac{\pi}{2} = \lim_{n\to\infty}\left(\frac{2}{1}\cdot\frac{2}{3}\cdot\frac{4}{3}\cdot\frac{4}{5}\cdot\frac{6}{5}\cdot\frac{6}{7}\cdot\cdots\cdot\frac{2n}{2n-1}\cdot\frac{2n}{2n+1}\right);$$
- an elegant proof that $\pi$ is irrational.

# Introduction

The concept of a *limit of a function* is closely related to that of a continuous function; roughly speaking, a function has a limit at a point $c$ if the function is defined near $c$ and can be extended to give a function which is continuous at $c$. We discuss such limits in Section 1.

In Section 2 we define various types of asymptotic behaviour of functions. For example, we show that if $n \in \mathbb{N}$, then $x^n/e^x \to 0$ as $x \to \infty$.

Section 3 returns to the topic of continuity and introduces an alternative definition, the so-called $\varepsilon$–$\delta$ definition of continuity. This definition is equivalent to the definition based on sequences, but it is more abstract. We also define several unusual functions, and establish their continuity properties, using either the $\varepsilon$–$\delta$ definition of continuity or the sequential definition, as appropriate. We then indicate that analogous definitions can be given of the 'limit' concepts introduced in Sections 1 and 2.

See Unit AA4, Section 2, for the sequential definition of continuity.

Finally, in Section 4 we discuss *uniform continuity*. This is a stronger form of continuity, defined using the $\varepsilon$–$\delta$ approach, and it will play an important role when we meet the integration of continuous functions.

## Study guide

The sections should be studied in their natural order. The notion of a limit is of fundamental importance to differentiation, so you should be sure to devote sufficient time to Section 1. Many of the results in Sections 1 and 2 are analogues of results on sequences and continuity in Units AA2 and AA4, so we omit their proofs.

# 1 Limits of functions

After working through this section, you should be able to:

(a) understand the statement $\lim_{x \to c} f(x) = l$, or $f(x) \to l$ as $x \to c$;

(b) appreciate the relationship between limits and continuity;

(c) use the Combination Rules, Composition Rule and Squeeze Rule to calculate limits of functions;

(d) understand the statements $\lim_{x \to c^+} f(x) = l$ and $\lim_{x \to c^-} f(x) = l$;

(e) use certain important limits to find other limits.

## 1.1 What is a limit of a function?

Sometimes we need to understand the behaviour of a function that is defined near a particular point, but not at the point itself. For example, the function

$$f(x) = \frac{\sin x}{x} \quad (x \in \mathbb{R} - \{0\})$$

arises when we prove that the sine function is differentiable. The graph of $f$ (see below) suggests that if $x$ takes values which are close to but different from 0, then $f(x)$ takes values which are close to 1.

See Unit AB2, Theorem 1.1.

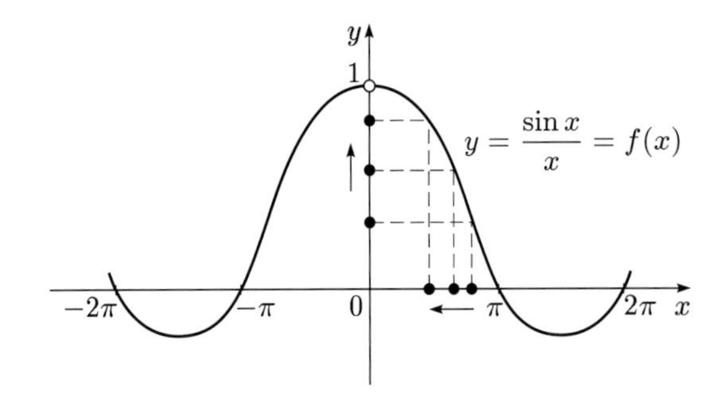


On the other hand, consider the function

$$g(x) = \sin \frac{1}{x} \quad (x \in \mathbb{R} - \{0\}).$$

In this case, when $x$ takes values close to 0, the values taken by $g(x)$ do not lie close to any *single* real number.

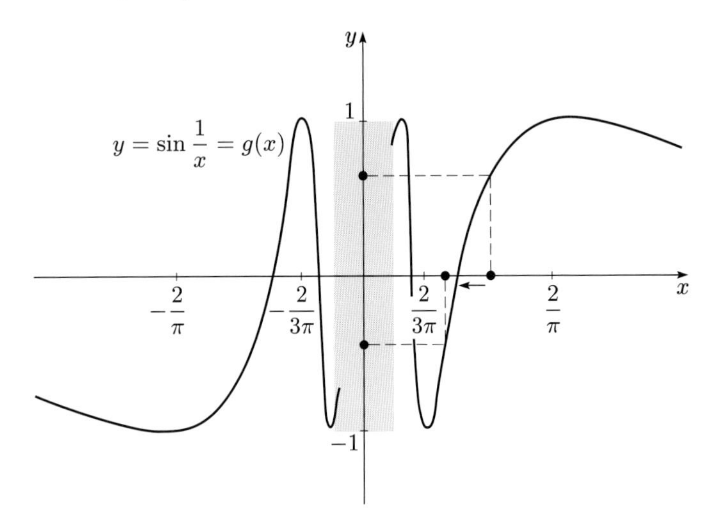


We say that the function $f$ has a *limit* as $x$ tends to 0, but the function $g$ does not. We now make this concept precise.

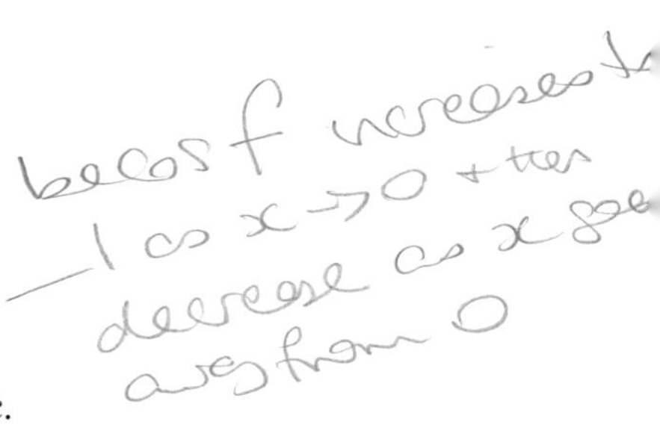

First we introduce the idea of a **punctured neighbourhood** of a point $c$. This is simply a bounded open interval with midpoint $c$, from which the point $c$ itself has been removed. We use the notation $N_r(c)$ for a punctured neighbourhood of length $2r$ with centre $c$:

$N_r(c)$
$c - r$ $c$ $c + r$

$$N_r(c) = (c - r, c) \cup (c, c + r), \quad \text{where } r > 0.$$

For example $N_1(3) = (2, 3) \cup (3, 4)$.

> **Definition** Let $f$ be a function defined on a punctured neighbourhood $N_r(c)$ of $c$. Then $f(x)$ **tends to the limit $l$ as $x$ tends to $c$** if
>
> for each sequence $\{x_n\}$ in $N_r(c)$ such that $x_n \to c$,
>
> $$f(x_n) \to l. \qquad (1.1)$$
>
> In this case, we write
>
> $$\lim_{x \to c} f(x) = l \quad \text{or} \quad f(x) \to l \text{ as } x \to c.$$

*Remarks*

1. Note that the limit $\lim_{x \to c} f(x)$, if it exists, does not depend on which punctured neighbourhood of $c$ is considered.

2. The above definition does not allow us to state that

$$\lim_{x\to 0} \sqrt{x}$$

exists, because the domain $[0,\infty)$ of $f(x) = \sqrt{x}$ does not contain any punctured neighbourhood of 0. Later in this section we introduce the concept of a *one-sided limit*, and see that $f(x) = \sqrt{x}$ has limit 0 as $x$ tends to 0 *from the right.*

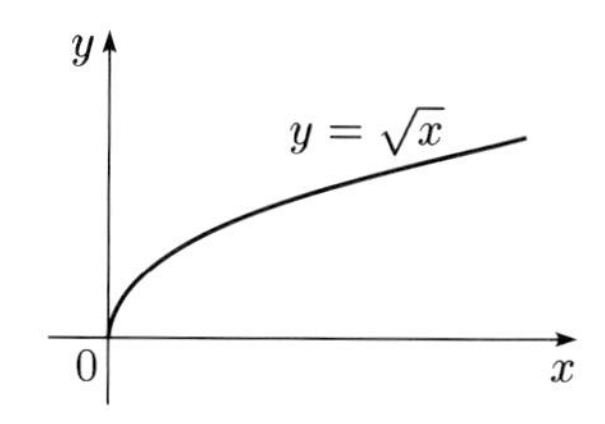


We now establish the limit of $(\sin x)/x$ discussed earlier.

**Theorem 1.1**

$$\lim_{x\to 0} \frac{\sin x}{x} = 1.$$

**Proof** The function $x \longmapsto (\sin x)/x$ is defined on each punctured neighbourhood of 0.

First we use the inequality

$$\sin x \le x, \quad \text{for } 0 < x \le \pi/2,$$

See Unit AA4, Section 2.

to deduce that

$$\frac{\sin x}{x} \le 1, \quad \text{for } 0 < x \le \pi/2. \tag{1.2}$$

Next we require the inequality

$$x \le \tan x, \quad \text{for } 0 < x < \pi/2, \tag{1.3}$$

which follows by comparing the area of a sector of a disc of radius 1 with that of a certain right-angled triangle which contains the sector, as shown in the figure.

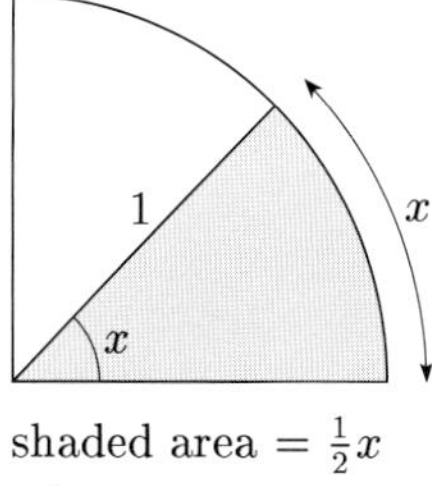


shaded area $= \frac{1}{2}x$

(a)

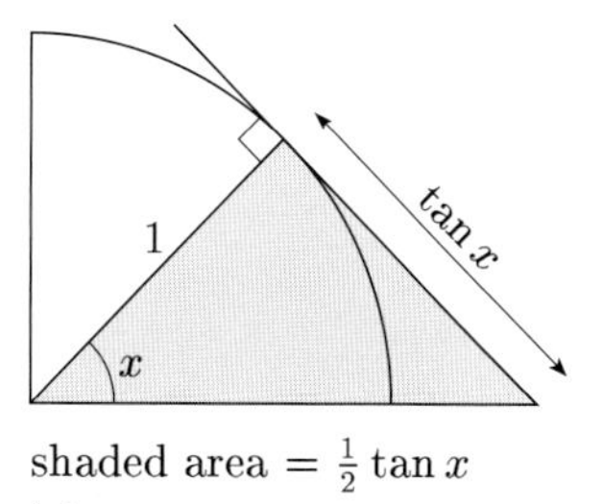


shaded area $= \frac{1}{2}\tan x$

(b)

A sector of a disc of radius $r$ with angle $\theta$ has area $\frac{1}{2}r^2\theta$.

Since $\cos x > 0$ for $0 < x < \pi/2$, we deduce from inequality (1.3) that

$$\cos x \le \frac{\sin x}{x}, \quad \text{for } 0 < x < \pi/2.$$

Thus, by inequality (1.2) and the fact that the functions $x \longmapsto \cos x$ and $x \longmapsto (\sin x)/x$ are both even,

We have $\cos(-x) = \cos x$ and $\dfrac{\sin(-x)}{-x} = \dfrac{\sin x}{x}$.

$$\cos x \le \frac{\sin x}{x} \le 1, \quad \text{for } 0 < |x| < \pi/2. \tag{1.4}$$

Now suppose that $\{x_n\}$ is any null sequence in the punctured neighbourhood $N_{\pi/2}(0)$. Then

$$\cos x_n \le \frac{\sin x_n}{x_n} \le 1, \quad \text{for } n = 1, 2, \ldots, \tag{1.5}$$

by inequality (1.4). Since $x_n \to 0$, we have $\cos x_n \to 1$, because the cosine function is continuous at 0 and $\cos 0 = 1$.

Hence, by inequality (1.5) and the Squeeze Rule for sequences,

See Unit AA2, Section 3.

$$\frac{\sin x_n}{x_n} \to 1 \text{ as } n \to \infty,$$

as required. ■

The limit in Theorem 1.1 was quite tricky to establish, but usually there are simpler ways to find limits. For example, we can determine many limits of functions by using the Combination Rules for sequences.

**Example 1.1** Prove that each of the following functions tends to a limit as $x$ tends to 2, and determine these limits.

(a) $f(x) = \dfrac{x^2 - 4}{x - 2}$ (b) $f(x) = \dfrac{x^3 - 3x - 2}{x^2 - 3x + 2}$

**Solution**

(a) The domain of $f$ is $\mathbb{R} - \{2\}$, so $f$ is defined on each punctured neighbourhood of 2. Also,

$$f(x) = \frac{x^2 - 4}{x - 2} = \frac{(x-2)(x+2)}{x - 2} = x + 2, \quad \text{for } x \neq 2.$$

We can cancel $x - 2$, since $x \neq 2$.

Thus if $\{x_n\}$ is any sequence in $\mathbb{R} - \{2\}$ such that $x_n \to 2$, then

$$f(x_n) = x_n + 2 \to 2 + 2 = 4 \text{ as } n \to \infty,$$

by the Sum Rule for sequences. Hence

$$\lim_{x \to 2} \frac{x^2 - 4}{x - 2} = 4.$$

(b) Since $x^2 - 3x + 2 = (x-2)(x-1)$, the domain of $f$ is $\mathbb{R} - \{1, 2\}$. Thus $f$ is defined on $N_1(2)$ and

$$f(x) = \frac{x^3 - 3x - 2}{x^2 - 3x + 2} = \frac{(x-2)(x^2 + 2x + 1)}{(x-2)(x-1)} = \frac{x^2 + 2x + 1}{x - 1},$$

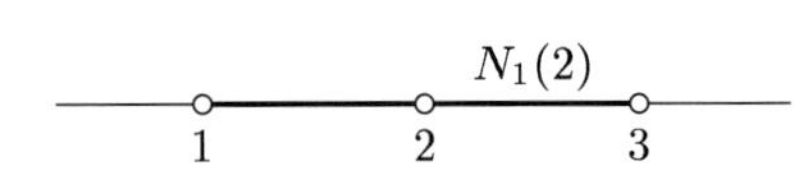


for $x \in N_1(2)$. Thus if $\{x_n\}$ lies in $N_1(2)$ and $x_n \to 2$, then

$$f(x_n) = \frac{x_n^2 + 2x_n + 1}{x_n - 1} \to \frac{4 + 4 + 1}{2 - 1} = 9,$$

by the Combination Rules for sequences. Hence

$$\lim_{x \to 2} \frac{x^3 - 3x - 2}{x^2 - 3x + 2} = 9. \quad ■$$

Later in this section we give further techniques for finding limits. Now we give a strategy for proving that a limit does *not* exist.

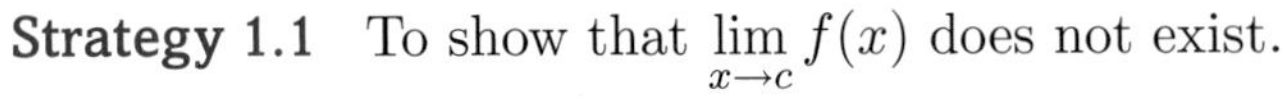

**Strategy 1.1** To show that $\lim_{x \to c} f(x)$ does not exist.

EITHER

1. find two sequences $\{x_n\}$ and $\{y_n\}$ which tend to $c$, but whose terms are not equal to $c$, such that $\{f(x_n)\}$ and $\{f(y_n)\}$ have different limits;

OR

2. find a sequence $\{x_n\}$ which tends to $c$, but whose terms are not equal to $c$, such that $f(x_n) \to \infty$ or $f(x_n) \to -\infty$.

**Example 1.2** Prove that each of the following functions does not tend to a limit as $x$ tends to 0.

(a) $f(x) = \sin(1/x)$ (b) $f(x) = 1/x$

**Solution**

(a) The function $f(x) = \sin(1/x)$ has domain $\mathbb{R} - \{0\}$. To prove that $f(x)$ does not tend to a limit as $x$ tends to 0, we choose two null sequences $\{x_n\}$ and $\{y_n\}$ in $\mathbb{R} - \{0\}$ such that

$$f(x_n) \to 1 \quad \text{whereas} \quad f(y_n) \to -1.$$

Here we use part 1 of Strategy 1.1.

To do this we use the facts that

$$\sin(2n\pi + \pi/2) = 1 \quad \text{and} \quad \sin(2n\pi + 3\pi/2) = -1, \quad \text{for } n \in \mathbb{Z}.$$

It follows that if we choose

$$x_n = \frac{1}{2n\pi + \pi/2} \quad \text{and} \quad y_n = \frac{1}{2n\pi + 3\pi/2}, \quad n = 1, 2, \ldots,$$

then $x_n \to 0$, $y_n \to 0$ and, for $n = 1, 2, \ldots$,

$$f(x_n) = \sin(1/x_n) = 1 \quad \text{and} \quad f(y_n) = \sin(1/y_n) = -1,$$

so

$$f(x_n) \to 1 \text{ as } n \to \infty \quad \text{and} \quad f(y_n) \to -1 \text{ as } n \to \infty.$$

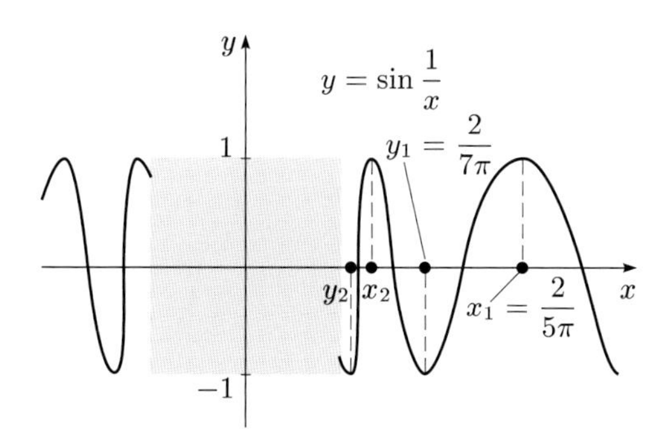


Hence $f(x) = \sin(1/x)$ does not tend to a limit as $x$ tends to 0.

(b) The function $f(x) = 1/x$ has domain $\mathbb{R} - \{0\}$. The sequence $\{1/n\}$ lies in $\mathbb{R} - \{0\}$ and tends to 0, but

Here we use part 2 of Strategy 1.1.

$$f(1/n) = \frac{1}{1/n} = n \to \infty \quad \text{as } n \to \infty.$$

Hence $f(x) = 1/x$ does not tend to a limit as $x$ tends to 0. ■

Here are some limits of functions for you to consider.

**Exercise 1.1** Determine whether each of the following limits exists, and evaluate those limits which do exist.

(a) $\displaystyle\lim_{x\to 0} \frac{x^2 + x}{x}$ (b) $\displaystyle\lim_{x\to 1} [x]$ (c) $\displaystyle\lim_{x\to 0} \log_e |x|$

Recall from Unit I1, Subsection 1.2, Frame 8, that $[x]$ is the integer part of $x$.

## 1.2 Limits and continuity

Consider the function

$$f(x) = \begin{cases} 1, & x \neq 0, \\ 0, & x = 0. \end{cases}$$

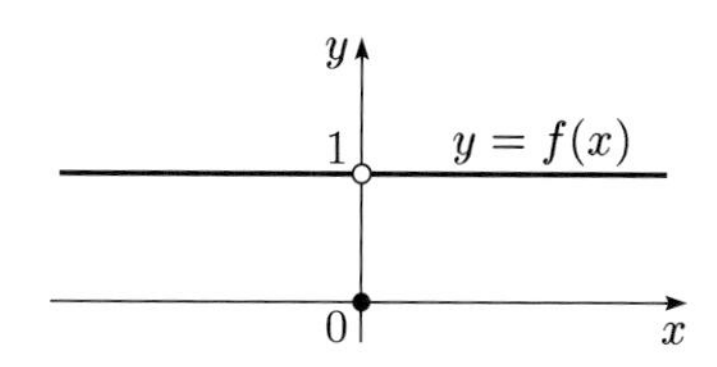


Does this function tend to a limit as $x$ tends to 0 and, if so, what is the limit?

Well, if $\{x_n\}$ is any null sequence with non-zero terms, then

$$f(x_n) = 1, \text{ for } n = 1, 2, \ldots, \quad \text{so} \quad f(x_n) \to 1 \text{ as } n \to \infty.$$

Hence

$$\lim_{x \to 0} f(x) = 1.$$

This example illustrates that the value of a limit $\lim_{x \to c} f(x)$ is not affected by the value of $f(c)$, if $f$ happens to be defined at $c$.

However, the following theorem shows that if $f$ is defined and *continuous* at $c$, then the value of the limit must be $f(c)$, and the converse statement is also true.

> **Theorem 1.2** Let $f$ be a function defined on an open interval $I$, with $c \in I$. Then
>
> $f$ is continuous at $c$
>
> if and only if
>
> $$\lim_{x \to c} f(x) = f(c).$$

The proof of Theorem 1.2 uses the fact that, in this situation, the definition of continuity of $f$ at $c$ is almost identical to the definition of the existence of $\lim_{x \to c} f(x)$, with this limit equal to $f(c)$. The only difference is that, in the former case, we allow the terms of the sequences $\{x_n\}$ which appear in the definition to equal $c$. We omit the details of this proof.

Theorem 1.2 makes it easy to calculate many limits of continuous functions. For example, to determine

$$\lim_{x \to 2} (3x^5 - 5x^2 + 1),$$

we use the fact that the function $f(x) = 3x^5 - 5x^2 + 1$ is continuous on $\mathbb{R}$, since $f$ is a polynomial. Hence, by Theorem 1.2,

$$\lim_{x \to 2} (3x^5 - 5x^2 + 1) = f(2) = 77.$$

As a further example, recall that the function

See Unit AA4, Subsection 2.1, Frame 16.

$$f(x) = \begin{cases} x^2 \sin(1/x), & x \neq 0, \\ 0, & x = 0, \end{cases}$$

is continuous at 0. Thus, by Theorem 1.2,

$$\lim_{x \to 0} x^2 \sin(1/x) = 0.$$

On the other hand, we saw in Example 1.2(a) that

$$\lim_{x \to 0} \sin(1/x) \text{ does not exist.}$$

It follows from Theorem 1.2 that, no matter how we try to extend the domain of the function $f(x) = \sin(1/x)$ to include $x = 0$, we can never obtain a continuous function.

**Exercise 1.2** Use Theorem 1.2 to determine the following limits.

(a) $\lim_{x \to 2} \sqrt{x}$ (b) $\lim_{x \to \pi/2} \sqrt{\sin x}$ (c) $\lim_{x \to 1} \dfrac{e^x}{1 + x}$

In the remainder of this unit we often use Theorem 1.2, but we do not always refer to it explicitly.

## 1.3 Rules for limits

As you might expect from your experiences with sequences, series and continuous functions, limits can often be found by using various rules. First we state the Combination Rules. These can be deduced from the corresponding rules for sequences; we omit the details.

**Combination Rules** If $\lim_{x\to c} f(x) = l$ and $\lim_{x\to c} g(x) = m$, then:

**Sum Rule** $\lim_{x\to c}(f(x) + g(x)) = l + m$;

**Multiple Rule** $\lim_{x\to c} \lambda f(x) = \lambda l$, for $\lambda \in \mathbb{R}$;

**Product Rule** $\lim_{x\to c} f(x)g(x) = lm$;

**Quotient Rule** $\lim_{x\to c} f(x)/g(x) = l/m$, provided that $m \neq 0$.

For example, since

$$\lim_{x\to 0} \frac{\sin x}{x} = 1 \quad \text{and} \quad \lim_{x\to 0}(x^2 + 1) = 1,$$

we have, by the Combination Rules,

$$\lim_{x\to 0}\left(\frac{\sin x}{x} + 2(x^2 + 1)\right) = 1 + 2 \times 1 = 3.$$

Next we discuss the composition of limits. For example, consider the behaviour of

$$\frac{\sin(x^2)}{x^2},$$

as $x$ tends to 0. This function can be written in the form

$$\frac{\sin(x^2)}{x^2} = \frac{\sin u}{u}, \quad \text{where } u = x^2.$$

Now

$$u = x^2 \to 0 \text{ as } x \to 0 \quad \text{and} \quad \frac{\sin u}{u} \to 1 \text{ as } u \to 0,$$

which suggests that

$$\frac{\sin(x^2)}{x^2} \to 1 \text{ as } x \to 0.$$

To justify this composition of limits, we use the Composition Rule.

**Composition Rule** If $\lim_{x\to c} f(x) = l$ and $\lim_{x\to l} g(x) = L$, then

$$\lim_{x\to c} g(f(x)) = L,$$

provided that

EITHER $f(x) \neq l$, for $x$ in some $N_r(c)$, where $r > 0$,

OR $g$ is defined at $l$ and continuous at $l$.

Note that the second limit is a limit as $x \to l$.

Perhaps surprisingly, the Composition Rule is false if we omit *both* of the provisos. For example, if

$$f(x) = 1 \quad \text{and} \quad g(x) = \begin{cases} 2, & x \neq 1, \\ 0, & x = 1, \end{cases}$$

then

$$\lim_{x\to 0} f(x) = 1 \quad \text{and} \quad \lim_{x\to 1} g(x) = 2, \quad \text{but} \quad \lim_{x\to 1} g(f(x)) = 0 \neq 2.$$

However, in nearly all cases in practice and in all the examples you will meet later in this course, at least one of the provisos holds. So you may assume that the following strategy can be applied.

**Strategy 1.2** To use the Composition Rule.

To evaluate a limit of a function of the form $g(f(x))$, as $x \to c$:

1. substitute $u = f(x)$ and show that, for some $l$,
$$u = f(x) \to l \text{ as } x \to c;$$
2. show that, for some $L$,
$$g(u) \to L \text{ as } u \to l;$$
3. deduce that
$$g(f(x)) \to L \text{ as } x \to c.$$

The following example illustrates how we apply this strategy.

**Example 1.3** Determine the following limits.

(a) $\displaystyle\lim_{x\to 0} \frac{\sin(\frac{1}{2}x)}{\frac{1}{2}x}$ (b) $\displaystyle\lim_{x\to 0} \left(1 + \left(\frac{\sin x}{x}\right)^2\right)$

**Solution**

(a) We can write

$$\frac{\sin(\frac{1}{2}x)}{\frac{1}{2}x} = g(f(x)), \quad \text{where } f(x) = \tfrac{1}{2}x \text{ and } g(x) = \frac{\sin x}{x}.$$

Substituting $u = f(x) = \frac{1}{2}x$, we have

$$u = \tfrac{1}{2}x \to 0 \text{ as } x \to 0,$$

$$g(u) = \frac{\sin u}{u} \to 1 \text{ as } u \to 0.$$

Thus, by the Composition Rule,

$$g(f(x)) = \frac{\sin(\frac{1}{2}x)}{\frac{1}{2}x} \to 1 \text{ as } x \to 0.$$

Here the first proviso of the Composition Rule holds:
$f(x) \neq 0, \quad \text{for } x \in N_1(0).$

(b) We can write

$$1 + \left(\frac{\sin x}{x}\right)^2 = g(f(x)), \quad \text{where } f(x) = \frac{\sin x}{x} \text{ and } g(x) = 1 + x^2.$$

Substituting $u = f(x) = \dfrac{\sin x}{x}$, we obtain

$$u = \frac{\sin x}{x} \to 1 \text{ as } x \to 0,$$

$$g(u) = 1 + u^2 \to 1 + 1 = 2 \text{ as } u \to 1.$$

Thus, by the Composition Rule,

$$g(f(x)) = 1 + \left(\frac{\sin x}{x}\right)^2 \to 2 \text{ as } x \to 0. \quad \blacksquare$$

Here both provisos of the Composition Rule hold:

$f(x) \neq 1, \quad$ for $x \in N_1(0)$,

and

$g$ is continuous at 1.

**Exercise 1.3** Use the Combination Rules and the Composition Rule to determine the following limits.

(a) $\lim\limits_{x\to 0} \dfrac{\sin x}{2x + x^2}$ (b) $\lim\limits_{x\to 0} \dfrac{\sin(\sin x)}{\sin x}$ (c) $\lim\limits_{x\to 0} \left(\dfrac{x}{\sin x}\right)^{1/2}$

There is also a Squeeze Rule for limits, analogous to the Squeeze Rules for sequences and continuous functions, whose proof we omit.

> **Squeeze Rule** Let $f$, $g$ and $h$ be functions defined on $N_r(c)$, for some $r > 0$. If
> (a) $g(x) \leq f(x) \leq h(x)$, for $x \in N_r(c)$,
> (b) $\lim\limits_{x\to c} g(x) = \lim\limits_{x\to c} h(x) = l$,
>
> then
>
> $$\lim_{x\to c} f(x) = l.$$

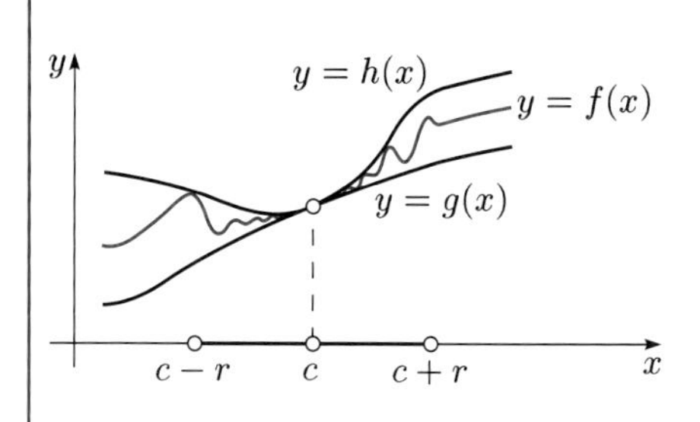


In the proof of Theorem 1.1, we showed that $\lim\limits_{x\to 0} (\sin x)/x = 1$, using the inequalities

$$\cos x \leq \frac{\sin x}{x} \leq 1, \quad \text{for } 0 < |x| < \pi/2.$$

This was, in essence, an application of the Squeeze Rule. In the next exercise the Squeeze Rule is used to establish another important limit.

**Exercise 1.4**

(a) Use the inequalities

$$1 + x \leq e^x \leq \frac{1}{1-x}, \quad \text{for } |x| < 1,$$

See Unit AA4, Subsection 2.3.

to show that

$$1 - \frac{|x|}{1-x} \leq \frac{e^x - 1}{x} \leq 1 + \frac{|x|}{1-x}, \quad \text{for } 0 < |x| < 1.$$

(b) Deduce from part (a) that

$$\lim_{x\to 0} \frac{e^x - 1}{x} = 1.$$

The limit found in Exercise 1.4 is one of the basic limits we often use. Here we record three such limits for future reference.

> **Theorem 1.3 Three basic limits**
>
> (a) $\lim\limits_{x\to 0} \dfrac{\sin x}{x} = 1$
>
> (b) $\lim\limits_{x\to 0} \dfrac{1 - \cos x}{x} = 0$
>
> (c) $\lim\limits_{x\to 0} \dfrac{e^x - 1}{x} = 1$

The first limit was evaluated in Theorem 1.1.

The second limit is evaluated in Exercise 1.7(b).

## 1.4 One-sided limits

Earlier, we mentioned that $\lim_{x \to 0} \sqrt{x}$ is not defined because the function $f(x) = \sqrt{x}$ is not defined on any punctured neighbourhood of 0. However, this function does tend to 0 as $x$ tends to 0 *from the right.*

> **Definition** Let $f$ be a function defined on $(c, c+r)$, for some $r > 0$. Then $f(x)$ **tends to the limit $l$ as $x$ tends to $c$ from the right** if
>
> for each sequence $\{x_n\}$ in $(c, c+r)$ such that $x_n \to c$,
>
> $f(x_n) \to l$.
>
> In this case, we write
>
> $$\lim_{x \to c^+} f(x) = l \quad \text{or} \quad f(x) \to l \text{ as } x \to c^+.$$
>
> There is a similar definition for a limit **as $x$ tends to $c$ from the left**, in which $(c, c+r)$ is replaced by $(c-r, c)$. In this case, we write
>
> $$\lim_{x \to c^-} f(x) = l \quad \text{or} \quad f(x) \to l \text{ as } x \to c^-.$$

We also refer to

$$\lim_{x \to c^+} f(x) \quad \text{and} \quad \lim_{x \to c^-} f(x)$$

as *right* and *left limits*, respectively.

Sometimes both right and left limits exist, but are different, as the next example shows.

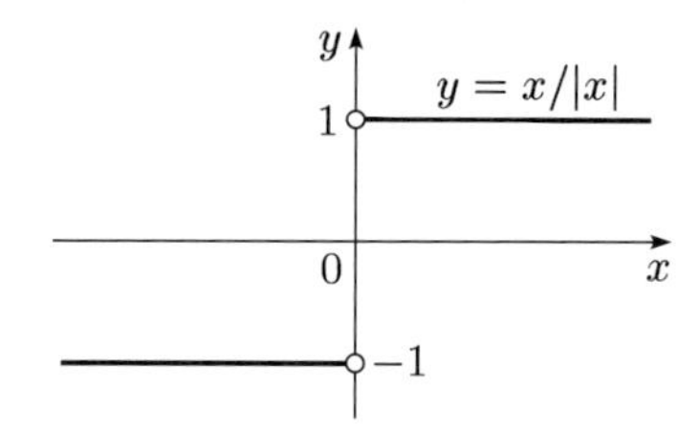


**Example 1.4** Prove that the following function tends to different limits as $x$ tends to 0 from the right and from the left:

$$f(x) = \frac{x}{|x|} \quad (x \in \mathbb{R} - \{0\}).$$

**Solution**

The function $f$ is defined on $(0, 1)$ and $f(x) = 1$ on this open interval. Thus if $\{x_n\}$ is a null sequence in $(0, 1)$, then

If $x > 0$, then $|x| = x$.

$$\lim_{n \to \infty} f(x_n) = \lim_{n \to \infty} 1 = 1.$$

Hence $\lim_{x \to 0^+} f(x) = 1$.

Similarly, $f$ is defined on $(-1, 0)$ and $f(x) = -1$ on this interval. Thus if $\{x_n\}$ is a null sequence in $(-1, 0)$, then

If $x < 0$, then $|x| = -x$.

$$\lim_{n \to \infty} f(x_n) = \lim_{n \to \infty} -1 = -1.$$

Hence $\lim_{x \to 0^-} f(x) = -1$.

Since $-1 \neq 1$, the limits of $f(x)$ as $x$ tends to 0 from the right and from the left are different. ■

The relationship between one-sided limits and ordinary limits is given by the following result, whose proof we omit.

> **Theorem 1.4** Let the function $f$ be defined on $N_r(c)$, for some $r > 0$. Then
>
> $$\lim_{x \to c} f(x) = l$$
>
> if and only if
>
> $$\lim_{x \to c^+} f(x) = \lim_{x \to c^-} f(x) = l.$$

Analogues of the Combination Rules, the Composition Rule (and Strategy 1.2) and the Squeeze Rule can also be used to determine one-sided limits. In the statements of these rules, we simply replace $\lim\limits_{x\to c}$ by $\lim\limits_{x\to c^+}$ or $\lim\limits_{x\to c^-}$, and replace $N_r(c)$ by $(c, c+r)$ or $(c-r, c)$, as appropriate.

Also, Strategy 1.1 can be adapted to show that a one-sided limit does *not* exist.

There is also a version of Theorem 1.2 for one-sided limits, as follows.

**Theorem 1.5** Let $f$ be a function whose domain is an interval $I$ with a finite left-hand endpoint $c$ that lies in $I$. Then

$f$ is continuous at $c$

if and only if

$$\lim_{x\to c^+} f(x) = f(c).$$

Thus $I$ can have the form $[c, \infty)$, $[c, b)$ or $[c, b]$, where $b > c$.

There is an analogous result for left limits.

For example, it follows from Theorem 1.5 that $\lim\limits_{x\to 0^+} \sqrt{x} = 0$, as claimed earlier, since $f(x) = \sqrt{x}$ has domain $[0, \infty)$ and is continuous at 0.

**Exercise 1.5** Prove the following.

(a) $\displaystyle\lim_{x\to 0^+}\left(\frac{\sin x}{x} + \sqrt{x}\right) = 1$ (b) $\displaystyle\lim_{x\to 0^+}\frac{\sin\sqrt{x}}{\sqrt{x}} = 1$

# Further exercises

**Exercise 1.6** Determine whether each of the following limits exists, and evaluate those limits which do exist.

(a) $\displaystyle\lim_{x\to 1}\frac{x^3-1}{x-1}$ (b) $\displaystyle\lim_{x\to 1}\frac{x^3-1}{|x-1|}$ (c) $\displaystyle\lim_{x\to 2} e^{x^2}$ (d) $\displaystyle\lim_{x\to 0^+}\frac{\cos(1/x^2)}{x}$

Hint: In part (a), use the identity $x^3 - 1 = (x-1)(x^2+x+1)$.

**Exercise 1.7** Determine the following limits.

(a) $\displaystyle\lim_{x\to 0}\left(\sin x + \frac{e^x - 1}{x}\right)$ (b) $\displaystyle\lim_{x\to 0}\frac{1-\cos x}{x}$

(c) $\displaystyle\lim_{x\to 0}\frac{e^{|x|}-1}{|x|}$ (d) $\displaystyle\lim_{x\to 1^-}\frac{x^3-1}{|x-1|}$

Hint: In part (b), use the identity $\cos x = 1 - 2\sin^2(\frac{1}{2}x)$.

# 2 Asymptotic behaviour of functions

After working through this section, you should be able to:

(a) understand the statements $f(x)\to\infty$ as $x\to c$ (or $c^+$ or $c^-$) and $f(x)\to l$ as $x\to\infty$ (or $-\infty$);

(b) use the Reciprocal Rule, the Combination Rules, the Squeeze Rule and the Composition Rule to determine the *asymptotic behaviour* of functions.

In our discussion of graph sketching, we described several types of *asymptotic behaviour* (that is, behaviour of a function when the domain variable or codomain variable becomes arbitrarily large), such as:

See Unit I1, Sections 2, 3 and 4.

$$\frac{1}{x} \to \infty \text{ as } x \to 0^+ \quad \text{and} \quad e^x \to \infty \text{ as } x \to \infty.$$

In this section we define such statements formally and describe various relationships between them.

## 2.1 Functions which tend to infinity

Earlier we defined $f(x) \to l$ as $x \to c$ in terms of the behaviour of sequences. We can define

$$f(x) \to \infty \text{ as } x \to c$$

in a similar way.

In this course we do not use the notation

$$\lim_{x \to c} f(x) = \infty.$$

**Definition** Let the function $f$ be defined on $N_r(c)$, for some $r > 0$. Then $f(x)$ **tends to $\infty$ as $x$ tends to $c$** if

for each sequence $\{x_n\}$ in $N_r(c)$ such that $x_n \to c$,

$$f(x_n) \to \infty.$$

In this case, we write

$$f(x) \to \infty \text{ as } x \to c.$$

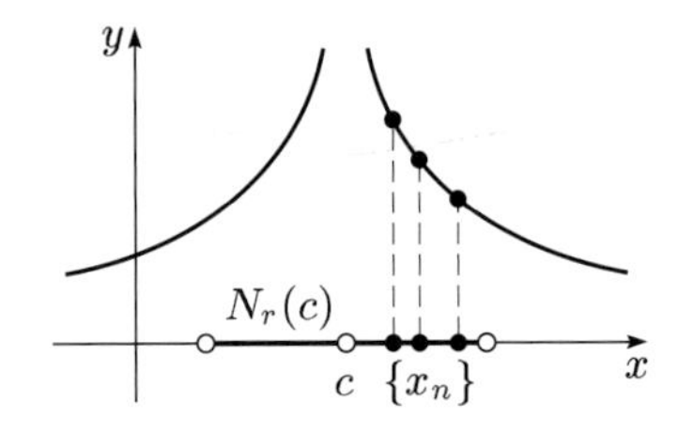


The statements

$$f(x) \to -\infty \text{ as } x \to c,$$
$$f(x) \to \infty \text{ (or } -\infty) \text{ as } x \to c^+ \text{ (or } c^-),$$

are defined similarly, with $\infty$ replaced by $-\infty$ and $N_r(c)$ replaced by the open interval $(c, c+r)$ or $(c-r, c)$, where $r > 0$, as appropriate.

There is a version of the Reciprocal Rule which relates functions that tend to infinity and functions that tend to 0.

The Reciprocal Rule for sequences is in Unit AA2, Section 4.

**Reciprocal Rule** If the function $f$ satisfies

(a) $f(x) > 0$ for $x \in N_r(c)$, for some $r > 0$,

(b) $f(x) \to 0$ as $x \to c$,

then

$$1/f(x) \to \infty \text{ as } x \to c.$$

For example,

$$1/x^2 \to \infty \text{ as } x \to 0,$$

because $f(x) = x^2 > 0$ for $x \in \mathbb{R} - \{0\}$, and $\lim_{x \to 0} x^2 = 0$.

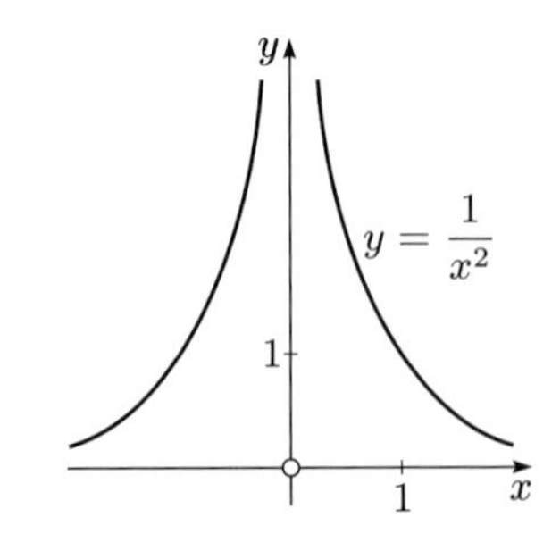


The Reciprocal Rule can also be applied with $x \to c$ replaced by $x \to c^+$ or $x \to c^-$, and $N_r(c)$ replaced by $(c, c+r)$ or $(c-r, c)$, as appropriate. For example, we have

$$1/x \to \infty \text{ as } x \to 0^+,$$

because $f(x) = x > 0$ for $x \in (0, \infty)$, and $\lim_{x \to 0^+} x = 0$.

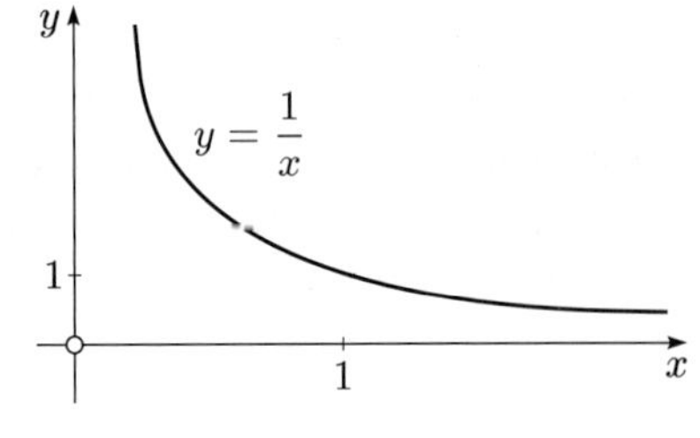

**Exercise 2.1** Prove that

(a) $\dfrac{1}{|x|} \to \infty$ as $x \to 0$;

(b) $\dfrac{\sin x}{x^3} \to \infty$ as $x \to 0$;

(c) $\dfrac{1}{x^3 - 1} \to \infty$ as $x \to 1^+$.

There are also versions of the Combination Rules and the Squeeze Rule for functions which tend to $\infty$ (or $-\infty$) as $x$ tends to $c$, $c^+$ or $c^-$. Here we state the Combination Rules for functions which tend to $\infty$ as $x$ tends to $c$.

> **Combination Rules** If $f(x) \to \infty$ as $x \to c$ and $g(x) \to \infty$ as $x \to c$, then:
>
> **Sum Rule** $f(x) + g(x) \to \infty$ as $x \to c$;
>
> **Multiple Rule** $\lambda f(x) \to \infty$ as $x \to c$, for $\lambda \in \mathbb{R}^+$;
>
> **Product Rule** $f(x)g(x) \to \infty$ as $x \to c$.

These rules are analogous to the corresponding rules for sequences which tend to infinity.

See Unit AA2, Section 4.

## 2.2 Behaviour as $x$ tends to infinity

Next, we define various types of behaviour of real functions $f(x)$ as $x \to \infty$ or as $x \to -\infty$. To avoid repetition, in the following definition we allow the letter $l$ to denote either a real number or one of the symbols $\infty$ or $-\infty$.

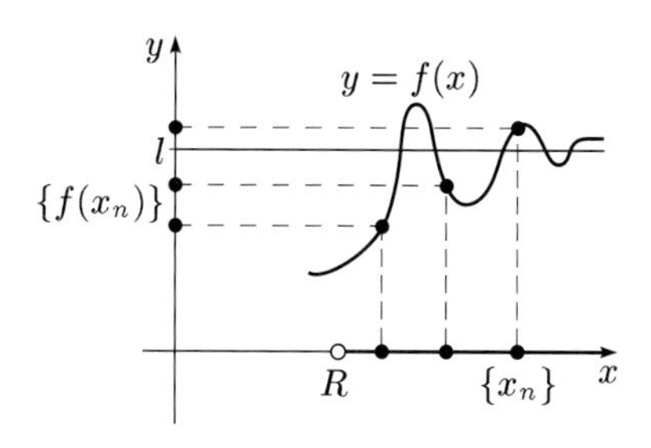


> **Definition** Let the function $f$ be defined on $(R, \infty)$, for some real number $R$. Then $f(x)$ **tends to $l$ as $x$ tends to $\infty$** if
>
> for each sequence $\{x_n\}$ in $(R, \infty)$ such that $x_n \to \infty$,
>
> $f(x_n) \to l$.
>
> In this case, we write
>
> $f(x) \to l$ as $x \to \infty$.

The statement

$$f(x) \to l \text{ as } x \to -\infty$$

is defined similarly, with $\infty$ replaced by $-\infty$, and $(R, \infty)$ replaced by $(-\infty, R)$.

Note that $f(x) \to l$ as $x \to -\infty$ is equivalent to $f(-x) \to l$ as $x \to \infty$.

When $l$ is a real number, we also use the notations

$$\lim_{x \to \infty} f(x) = l \quad \text{and} \quad \lim_{x \to -\infty} f(x) = l.$$

Once again, we can use versions of the Reciprocal Rule and the Combination Rules to obtain results about the behaviour of given functions as $x \to \infty$ or $-\infty$. The new versions of these rules are obtained from the Reciprocal Rule and the Combination Rules in Subsection 2.1 and the Combination Rules in Subsection 1.3 by replacing $c$ by $\infty$ or $-\infty$, and $N_r(c)$ by $(R, \infty)$ or $(-\infty, R)$, as appropriate.

Many results about the behaviour of functions $f(x)$ as $x$ tends to $\infty$ or $-\infty$ are derived from the following two basic facts, often by using the Combination Rules and the Reciprocal Rule.

**Theorem 2.1 Basic asymptotic behaviour**

If $n \in \mathbb{N}$, then

(a) $x^n \to \infty$ as $x \to \infty$,

(b) $\dfrac{1}{x^n} \to 0$ as $x \to \infty$.

We can use Theorem 2.1, together with the Combination Rules and the Reciprocal Rule, to determine the asymptotic behaviour of various functions defined by quotients. For example, consider the behaviour of $x/(x^2+1)$ as $x \to \infty$. Here the dominant term is $x^2$, so we divide both the numerator and the denominator by $x^2$ to give

$$\frac{x}{x^2+1} = \frac{1/x}{1+1/x^2} \to \frac{0}{1+0} = 0 \text{ as } x \to \infty,$$

by Theorem 2.1(b) and the Combination Rules.

Determining the asymptotic behaviour of functions defined by quotients is similar to determining the behaviour of sequences defined by quotients; see Unit AA2, Section 3.

**Exercise 2.2** Prove that:

(a) $\displaystyle\lim_{x\to\infty} \frac{2x^3+x}{x^3} = 2$; (b) $\dfrac{2x^3+1}{x^2} \to \infty$ as $x \to \infty$.

There are also versions of the Squeeze Rule for functions as $x$ tends to infinity, which have some important applications.

**Squeeze Rule** Let $f$, $g$ and $h$ be functions defined on some interval $(R, \infty)$.

(a) If

1. $g(x) \le f(x) \le h(x)$, for $x \in (R, \infty)$,
2. $\displaystyle\lim_{x\to\infty} g(x) = \lim_{x\to\infty} h(x) = l$,

where $l$ is a real number, then

$$\lim_{x\to\infty} f(x) = l.$$

(b) If

1. $f(x) \ge g(x)$, for $x \in (R, \infty)$,
2. $g(x) \to \infty$ as $x \to \infty$,

then

$$f(x) \to \infty \text{ as } x \to \infty.$$

The two versions of the Squeeze Rule for sequences are in Unit AA2, Sections 3 and 4.

**Exercise 2.3** Use the Squeeze Rule to determine the behaviour of the following function as $x \to \infty$:

$$f(x) = \frac{\sin(1/x)}{x}.$$

Hint: Use the fact that $-1 \le \sin(1/x) \le 1$ for $x \ne 0$.

In the next result, we collect together several standard results about the behaviour of particular functions as $x \to \infty$.

**Theorem 2.2**

(a) If $a_0, a_1, \ldots, a_{n-1} \in \mathbb{R}$, where $n \in \mathbb{N}$, and

$$p(x) = x^n + a_{n-1}x^{n-1} + \cdots + a_1 x + a_0,$$

then

$$p(x) \to \infty \text{ as } x \to \infty \quad \text{and} \quad \frac{1}{p(x)} \to 0 \text{ as } x \to \infty.$$

(b) For each $n = 0, 1, 2, \ldots$, we have

$$\frac{e^x}{x^n} \to \infty \text{ as } x \to \infty \quad \text{and} \quad \frac{x^n}{e^x} \to 0 \text{ as } x \to \infty.$$

(c) We have

$$\log_e x \to \infty \text{ as } x \to \infty,$$

but, for each constant $a > 0$, we have

$$\frac{\log_e x}{x^a} \to 0 \text{ as } x \to \infty.$$

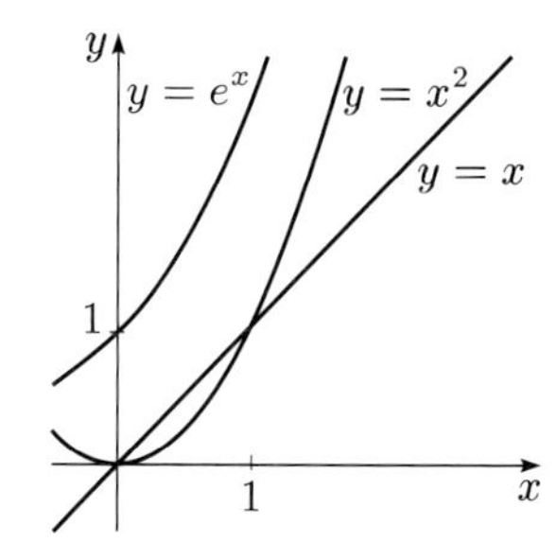


Part (b) tells us that, as $x$ tends to infinity, $e^x$ tends to infinity *faster* than any positive integer power of $x$, as illustrated. On the other hand, part (c) tells us that, as $x$ tends to infinity, $\log_e x$ tends to infinity *more slowly* than any positive power of $x$. Thus, in part (b) the dominant term is $e^x$, whereas in part (c) it is $x^a$.

**Proof of Theorem 2.2**

(a) We use the fact that all the zeros of the polynomial $p$ must lie in the interval $(-M, M)$, where $M = 1 + \max\{|a_{n-1}|, \ldots, |a_1|, |a_0|\}$, and

See Unit AA4, Theorem 3.3 and Exercise 3.9.

$$p(x) > 0, \quad \text{for } x \in (M, \infty). \tag{2.1}$$

Now,

$$p(x) = x^n \left(1 + \frac{a_{n-1}}{x} + \cdots + \frac{a_0}{x^n}\right).$$

By Theorem 2.1(b) and the Combination Rules,

$$1 + \frac{a_{n-1}}{x} + \cdots + \frac{a_0}{x^n} \to 1 + 0 + \cdots + 0 = 1 \text{ as } x \to \infty. \tag{2.2}$$

Thus, for $x \in (M, \infty)$, we have

$$\frac{1}{p(x)} = \frac{1/x^n}{1 + a_{n-1}/x + \cdots + a_0/x^n} \to \frac{0}{1} = 0 \text{ as } x \to \infty,$$

by statement (2.2), Theorem 2.1(b) and the Quotient Rule for limits. We deduce, by statement (2.1) and the Reciprocal Rule, that

$$p(x) \to \infty \text{ as } x \to \infty.$$

(b) Let $n$ be a fixed non-negative integer. We use the power series representation

$$e^x = 1 + x + \frac{x^2}{2!} + \cdots + \frac{x^n}{n!} + \frac{x^{n+1}}{(n+1)!} + \cdots,$$

See Unit AA3, Section 4.

which we know to be valid for $x \geq 0$. Since $x \geq 0$, all the terms in the above series are non-negative, so

$$e^x \geq \frac{x^{n+1}}{(n+1)!}, \quad \text{for } x \geq 0.$$

Hence, for $x > 0$,

$$\frac{e^x}{x^n} \geq \frac{x}{(n+1)!} \quad \text{and} \quad 0 \leq \frac{x^n}{e^x} \leq \frac{(n+1)!}{x}.$$

It follows by Theorem 2.1 and the Squeeze Rule that

$$\frac{e^x}{x^n} \to \infty \text{ as } x \to \infty \quad \text{and} \quad \frac{x^n}{e^x} \to 0 \text{ as } x \to \infty.$$

(c) We deduce that

$$\log_e x \to \infty \text{ as } x \to \infty$$

by applying the Inverse Function Rule strategy to $f(x) = e^x$.

See Unit AA4, Strategy 4.1.

Now let $a$ be any positive constant. Since $x^a = \exp(a \log_e x)$, we make the substitution $t = a \log_e x$, so that $x^a = e^t$. For $x > 0$, this gives

Here we are using a version of the Composition Rule discussed in the next subsection.

$$\frac{\log_e x}{x^a} = \frac{t/a}{e^t} = \frac{t}{ae^t}. \tag{2.3}$$

Since $a > 0$, we have

$$t = a \log_e x \to \infty \text{ as } x \to \infty, \tag{2.4}$$

and, by part (b) with $n = 1$ and the Multiple Rule,

$$\frac{t}{ae^t} \to 0 \text{ as } t \to \infty. \tag{2.5}$$

Hence, by statements (2.3), (2.4) and (2.5), we have

$$\frac{\log_e x}{x^a} = \frac{t}{ae^t} \to 0 \text{ as } x \to \infty,$$

as required. ■

**Exercise 2.4** Use the results of Theorem 2.2 and the appropriate rules to determine the behaviour of the following functions as $x \to \infty$.

(a) $f(x) = \dfrac{e^x}{x^2} + \dfrac{3x^2}{\log_e x}$

(b) $f(x) = \dfrac{\log_e x}{e^x}$

Hint: Express $(\log_e x)/e^x$ in terms of $(\log_e x)/x$ and $x/e^x$.

(c) $f(x) = \dfrac{2e^x - x^2}{e^x + \log_e x}$

## 2.3 Composing asymptotic behaviour

Earlier we gave the Composition Rule for limits and Strategy 1.2 for using it. This strategy can be used to compose *all* the types of asymptotic behaviour introduced in this unit, provided that we allow the letters $l$ and $L$ to denote either a real number or one of the symbols $\infty$ or $-\infty$.

See page 11.

For example, consider the asymptotic behaviour of $e^{1/x}$ as $x \to 0^+$. We can write $e^{1/x} = g(f(x))$, where $f(x) = 1/x$ and $g(x) = e^x$. Substituting $u = f(x) = 1/x$, we have

$$u = f(x) = 1/x \to \infty \text{ as } x \to 0^+ \quad \text{(Reciprocal Rule)},$$
$$g(u) = e^u \to \infty \text{ as } u \to \infty \quad \text{(Theorem 2.2(b))}.$$

Thus we deduce by Strategy 1.2 that

$$g(f(x)) = e^{1/x} \to \infty \quad \text{as } x \to 0^+.$$

*Remark* There is often more than one way to establish asymptotic behaviour. In this example, we could instead argue as follows. We have

$$e^{1/x} \geq 1 + \frac{1}{x} > \frac{1}{x}, \quad \text{for } x > 0,$$

and we also know that $1/x \to \infty$ as $x \to 0^+$. Hence $e^{1/x} \to \infty$ as $x \to 0^+$, by the Squeeze Rule.

The inequality

$$e^x > 1 + x, \quad \text{for } x > 0,$$

follows from the series representation

$$e^x = 1 + x + \frac{1}{2!}x^2 + \cdots,$$

for $x > 0$.

**Exercise 2.5** Prove that:

(a) $e^{x^2}/x^2 \to \infty$ as $x \to \infty$;

(b) $\log_e(\log_e x) \to \infty$ as $x \to \infty$;

(c) $x\sin(1/x) \to 1$ as $x \to \infty$.

Hint: In part (c), use the substitution $u = 1/x$.

## Further exercise

**Exercise 2.6** Prove that:

(a) $\dfrac{1}{x^4} \to \infty$ as $x \to 0$; (b) $\cot x \to \infty$ as $x \to 0^+$;

(c) $e^x - x \to \infty$ as $x \to \infty$; (d) $\log_e x \to -\infty$ as $x \to 0^+$;

(e) $x + \sin x \to \infty$ as $x \to \infty$; (f) $x^x \to \infty$ as $x \to \infty$;

(g) $x^{1/x} \to 1$ as $x \to \infty$; (h) $\dfrac{x^2 + \log_e x}{x + e^x} \to 0$ as $x \to \infty$.

Hint: In parts (d), (f) and (g), use the identities

$$\log_e x = -\log_e(1/x) \quad \text{and} \quad a^x = \exp(x \log_e a).$$

# 3 Continuity—the classical definition

After working through this section, you should be able to:

(a) understand and use the $\varepsilon$–$\delta$ definition of continuity;

(b) describe functions which are highly discontinuous, or continuous but very irregular;

(c) understand and use the $\varepsilon$–$\delta$ definition of limit.

In Analysis Block A, we introduced a definition of continuity based on sequences, and we proved that most familiar functions are continuous on their domains, a fact which is not at all surprising. However, there are many functions of interest for which it is more difficult to establish continuity (or discontinuity).

Consider, for instance, the **Riemann function**, which has domain $\mathbb{R}$ and rule

$$f(x) = \begin{cases} 1/q, & \text{if } x \text{ is a rational } p/q, \text{ where } q > 0, \\ 0, & \text{if } x \text{ is irrational.} \end{cases}$$

In this section, we assume that all rationals $p/q$ are expressed in lowest terms; that is, the greatest common factor of $p$ and $q$ is 1.

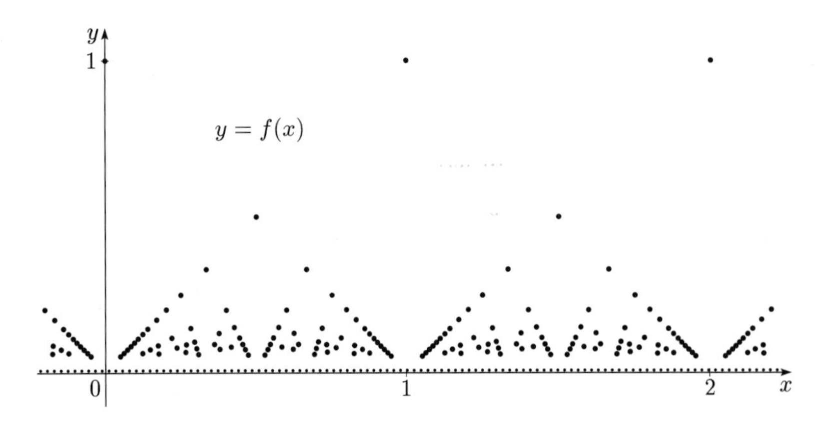


For example, $f(2/3) = 1/3$ and $f(\sqrt{2}) = 0$.

From this sketch of the graph of $f$ it is not clear whether the Riemann function is continuous at any point of $\mathbb{R}$, but we shall see that in fact it is continuous at infinitely many points and discontinuous at infinitely many points! When dealing with such unusual functions, it is useful to have available the alternative definition of continuity introduced in this section. This definition looks more abstract but is more effective in some cases.

See Theorem 3.3 below.

This definition of continuity emerged towards the end of the 19th century after many years of debate amongst mathematicians about the rigorous formulation of analysis as the foundations of calculus. At this time, the informal approach used in the 18th century, for instance by Euler, was increasingly found to be inadequate. For example, around 1820, Fourier used functions defined by infinite series to solve problems in the theory of heat. The properties of these series raised challenging questions about the meaning of convergence. This led to questions about the definitions of continuity, limits, differentiation and integration, and even the nature of the real numbers. These questions were not properly resolved until about 1870, after contributions by many mathematicians, including Bolzano, Cauchy, Riemann, Dirichlet, Dedekind, Weierstrass and Cantor.

Baron Joseph Fourier (1768–1830) was a French mathematician who introduced the idea of representing functions by infinite series of the form

$$\sum (a_n \cos(nx) + b_n \sin(nx)),$$

now known as *Fourier series*.

## 3.1 The $\varepsilon$–$\delta$ definition of continuity

Recall our sequential definition of continuity. This states that the function $f : A \longrightarrow \mathbb{R}$ is continuous at $c$, where $c \in A$, if

See Unit AA4, Section 2.

for each sequence $\{x_n\}$ in $A$ such that $x_n \to c$,

$f(x_n) \to f(c)$.

This definition uses sequences to formalise the intuitive idea that $f(x)$ approaches $f(c)$ as $x$ approaches the point $c$ in any manner.

The new definition formalises this idea in a somewhat different way, which we can describe in words as follows:

we can make $f(x)$ as close as we want to $f(c)$
by ensuring that $x$ is close enough to $c$.

The 'closeness' in this description is measured by two variables, $\varepsilon$ in the codomain and $\delta$ in the domain, which represent 'small' positive numbers.

> **Definition** Let the function $f$ have domain $A$ and let $c \in A$. Then $f$ is **continuous** at $c$ if
>
> for each $\varepsilon > 0$, there exists $\delta > 0$ such that
>
> $$|f(x) - f(c)| < \varepsilon, \quad \text{for all } x \in A \text{ with } |x - c| < \delta. \qquad (3.1)$$

*Remarks*

1. The above definition is quite subtle. It can be expressed in words as follows: no matter how small a positive number $\varepsilon$ we are *given*, we can *choose* a positive number $\delta$ such that if the distance between $x$ and $c$ is less than $\delta$, then the distance between $f(x)$ and $f(c)$ is less than $\varepsilon$. Thus statement (3.1) can be interpreted as an *implication*:

   if $x \in A$ and $|x - c| < \delta$, then $|f(x) - f(c)| < \varepsilon$.

The definition can be thought of as a game: player A gives player B a small number $\varepsilon > 0$; player B must then choose a sufficiently small number $\delta > 0$ so that statement (3.1) holds.

2. Note that

   $|f(x) - f(c)| < \varepsilon$ is equivalent to $f(c) - \varepsilon < f(x) < f(c) + \varepsilon$,
   $|x - c| < \delta$ is equivalent to $c - \delta < x < c + \delta$,

   as illustrated.

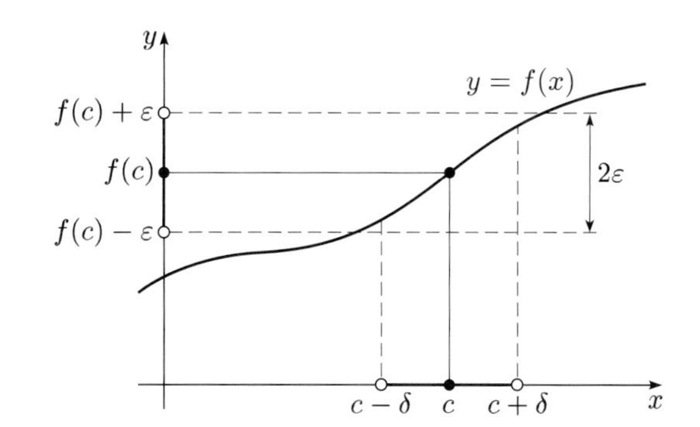


3. Usually the value of $\delta$ that we choose in order to make statement (3.1) true depends on the given value of $\varepsilon$; the smaller $\varepsilon$ is, the smaller $\delta$ has to be. The value of $\delta$ often depends also on the particular point $c$ at which we are checking continuity.

The method of applying the $\varepsilon$–$\delta$ definition of continuity depends on the nature of the function $f$. For some functions, including polynomial functions, we can use the following strategy.

> **Strategy 3.1** To use the $\varepsilon$–$\delta$ definition to prove continuity at a point.
>
> Let the function $f$ have domain $A$, with $c \in A$. To prove that $f$ is continuous at $c$, let $\varepsilon > 0$ be given and carry out the following.
>
> 1. Use algebraic manipulation to express the difference $f(x) - f(c)$ as a product of the form $(x - c)g(x)$.
> 2. Obtain an upper bound of the form $|g(x)| \leq M$, for $|x - c| \leq r$, where $r > 0$ is chosen so that $[c - r, c + r] \subset A$.
> 3. Use the fact that $|f(x) - f(c)| \leq M|x - c|$, for $|x - c| \leq r$, to choose $\delta > 0$ such that
>
> $$|f(x) - f(c)| < \varepsilon, \quad \text{for all } x \in A \text{ with } |x - c| < \delta.$$

Here we often use the Triangle Inequality; see Unit AA1, Section 2.

We use Strategy 3.1 in the following example.

**Example 3.1** Use the $\varepsilon$–$\delta$ definition to prove that $f(x) = x^2$ is continuous at $c = 2$.

**Solution** The domain of $f$ is $\mathbb{R}$.

Let $\varepsilon > 0$ be given. We want to choose $\delta > 0$, in terms of $\varepsilon$, such that

$$|f(x) - f(2)| < \varepsilon, \quad \text{for all } x \text{ with } |x - 2| < \delta. \qquad (3.2)$$

1. First we write

$$f(x) - f(2) = x^2 - 4 = (x - 2)(x + 2).$$

2. Next we obtain an upper bound for $|x + 2|$, when $x$ is near 2. If $|x - 2| \leq 1$, then $x$ lies in the closed interval $[1, 3]$, so

$$|x + 2| \leq |x| + 2 \quad \text{(Triangle Inequality)}$$
$$\leq 3 + 2 = 5.$$

Here we take $r = 1$; any $r > 0$ is suitable, but note that the resulting $M$ and $\delta$ depend on $r$.

3. Hence

$$|f(x) - f(2)| \leq 5|x - 2|, \quad \text{for } |x - 2| \leq 1.$$

So if $|x - 2| < \delta$, where $0 < \delta \leq 1$, then

$$|f(x) - f(2)| < 5\delta.$$

Now $5\delta \leq \varepsilon$ if and only if $\delta \leq \frac{1}{5}\varepsilon$. Thus, if we choose $\delta = \min\{1, \frac{1}{5}\varepsilon\}$, then

We define $\delta$ this way so that we have $0 < \delta \leq 1$ and $0 < \delta \leq \frac{1}{5}\varepsilon$.

$$|f(x) - f(2)| < 5\delta \leq 5 \times \tfrac{1}{5}\varepsilon = \varepsilon, \quad \text{for all } x \text{ with } |x - 2| < \delta,$$

which proves statement (3.2).

Thus $f$ is continuous at the point 2. ■

**Exercise 3.1** Use the $\varepsilon$–$\delta$ definition to prove that $f(x) = x^3$ is continuous at $c = 1$.

Hint: Note that $x^3 - 1 = (x - 1)(x^2 + x + 1)$.

Next we verify that the two definitions of continuity are equivalent.

**Theorem 3.1** The $\varepsilon$–$\delta$ definition and the sequential definition of continuity are equivalent.

**Proof** Let the function $f$ have domain $A$, with $c \in A$. First we assume that $f$ is continuous at $c$ according to the $\varepsilon$–$\delta$ definition. We want to deduce that, for each sequence $\{x_n\}$ in $A$ such that $x_n \to c$,

$$f(x_n) \to f(c). \qquad (3.3)$$

Let $\varepsilon > 0$ be given. Then there exists $\delta > 0$ such that

$$|f(x) - f(c)| < \varepsilon, \quad \text{for all } x \in A \text{ with } |x - c| < \delta. \qquad (3.4)$$

Since $x_n \to c$, there exists an integer $N$ such that

$$|x_n - c| < \delta, \quad \text{for all } n > N.$$

Hence, by statement (3.4),

$$|f(x_n) - f(c)| < \varepsilon, \quad \text{for all } n > N.$$

Thus statement (3.3) does indeed hold, so the sequential definition follows from the $\varepsilon$–$\delta$ definition.

Next suppose that $f$ is continuous at $c$ according to the sequential definition. We want to deduce that if $\varepsilon > 0$ is given, then there exists $\delta > 0$ such that statement (3.4) holds. Suppose that, for some $\varepsilon > 0$, there is *no* such $\delta > 0$. Then statement (3.4) must be false with $\delta = 1$, $\delta = \frac{1}{2}$, $\delta = \frac{1}{3}$, and so on. Hence, for each $n \in \mathbb{N}$ there exists $x_n \in A$ with $|x_n - c| < 1/n$ such that

This is a proof by contradiction.

$$|f(x_n) - f(c)| \geq \varepsilon. \qquad (3.5)$$

Now, the sequence $\{x_n\}$ lies in $A$ and $x_n \to c$. Thus, by the sequential definition of continuity, we have $\lim_{n\to\infty} f(x_n) = f(c)$, which contradicts statement (3.5). We deduce that the $\varepsilon$–$\delta$ definition of continuity follows from the sequential definition. ■

## 3.2 Continuity of strange functions

It is natural to ask which is the 'better' definition of continuity. It is difficult to give a definitive answer, but on the whole:

- when proving the continuity of simpler functions the sequential definition is usually easier, whereas the $\varepsilon$–$\delta$ definition can work better with more complicated functions;
- when proving discontinuity the sequential definition is usually easier.

For most of the functions that have appeared so far in this course, the points where the functions are continuous have been 'obvious'. However, there are many functions whose continuity properties are less clear. In this subsection, you will meet several interesting but quite complicated functions, and you will see that the $\varepsilon$–$\delta$ definition is an effective means of proving continuity, even when it is not possible to use Strategy 3.1.

### Dirichlet function and Riemann function

The first function we consider has a simple definition, but it is highly discontinuous. The **Dirichlet function** has domain $\mathbb{R}$ and rule

P. G. L. Dirichlet (1805–1859) was a German mathematician who made major contributions to analysis, number theory and mathematical physics.

$$f(x) = \begin{cases} 1, & \text{if } x \text{ is rational,} \\ 0, & \text{if } x \text{ is irrational.} \end{cases}$$

The graph of $f$ looks rather like two parallel lines, but each line has infinitely many 'holes' in it!

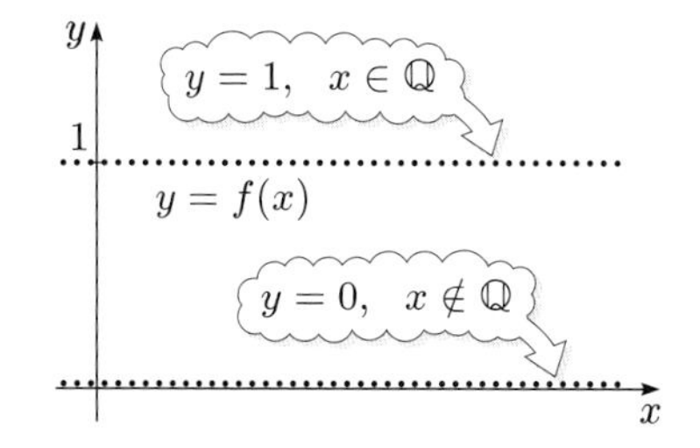


> **Theorem 3.2** The Dirichlet function is discontinuous at every point of $\mathbb{R}$.

**Proof** Let $c$ be any point of $\mathbb{R}$. We show that $f$ is discontinuous at $c$ by using the sequential definition.

If you are short of time, omit this proof.

By the Density Property of $\mathbb{R}$, each open interval of the form

See Unit AA1, Section 1.

$$(c - 1/n, c + 1/n), \quad \text{where } n \in \mathbb{N},$$

contains a rational $x_n$ and an irrational $y_n$. Considering the sequences $\{x_n\}$ and $\{y_n\}$, we have $x_n \to c$ and $y_n \to c$ by the Squeeze Rule for sequences, but

$$f(x_n) = 1 \quad \text{and} \quad f(y_n) = 0, \quad \text{for } n = 1, 2, \ldots.$$

Since $\{f(x_n)\}$ and $\{f(y_n)\}$ have different limits, $f$ is discontinuous at $c$. ■

See Unit AA4, Strategy 2.1.

Our next function shows even stranger behaviour. The **Riemann function** has domain $\mathbb{R}$ and rule

$$f(x) = \begin{cases} 1/q, & \text{if } x \text{ is a rational } p/q, \text{ where } q > 0, \\ 0, & \text{if } x \text{ is irrational.} \end{cases}$$

Bernhard Riemann (1826–1866) was a German mathematician who made major contributions to analysis, in particular to the connections between complex functions and geometry, and to integration. The 'Riemann hypothesis' is a famous unsolved problem which links complex functions to the distribution of the prime numbers.

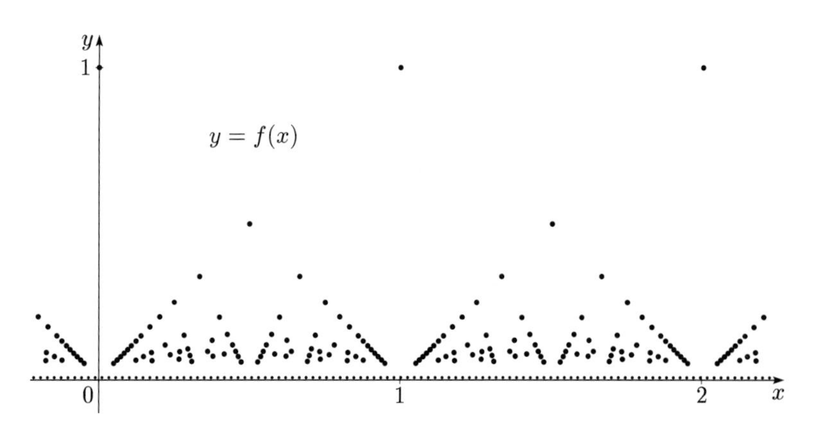


As mentioned earlier, it is not clear from this sketch of the graph of $f$ whether the Riemann function is continuous at any point of $\mathbb{R}$. In fact, it has the remarkable property that each open interval of $\mathbb{R}$ contains infinitely many points where $f$ is continuous and infinitely many points where $f$ is discontinuous.

**Theorem 3.3** The Riemann function is discontinuous at each rational point of $\mathbb{R}$ and continuous at each irrational point.

**Proof** Here we prove discontinuity using the sequential definition and we prove continuity using the $\varepsilon$–$\delta$ definition.

If you are short of time, omit this proof.

First we prove that $f$ is discontinuous at rational points. Let $c = p/q$, with $q > 0$ (where $p/q$ is expressed in lowest terms). Then, by the Density Property of $\mathbb{R}$, each open interval of the form

$$(c - 1/n, c + 1/n), \quad \text{where } n \in \mathbb{N},$$

contains an irrational number $x_n$. Considering the sequence $\{x_n\}$, we have $x_n \to c$ and $f(x_n) = 0$, for $n = 1, 2, \ldots$. Since $f(c) = 1/q \neq 0$, we have $f(x_n) \nrightarrow f(c)$, so $f$ is discontinuous at $c$.

The notation $\nrightarrow$ is read as 'does not tend to'.

Next we prove that $f$ is continuous at irrational points. Let $c$ be an irrational number in $\mathbb{R}$. We must prove that

for each $\varepsilon > 0$, there exists $\delta > 0$ such that

$$|f(x) - f(c)| < \varepsilon, \quad \text{for all } x \text{ with } |x - c| < \delta. \tag{3.6}$$

Let $\varepsilon > 0$ be given. Since $c$ is irrational, we have $f(c) = 0$. Also, $f(x) \geq 0$ for all $x$ in $\mathbb{R}$, so statement (3.6) can be rewritten as

$$f(x) < \varepsilon, \quad \text{for all } x \text{ with } |x - c| < \delta. \tag{3.7}$$

To obtain such a $\delta$, we first choose a positive integer $N$ such that $1/N < \varepsilon$. Then we let $S_N$ denote the set of rationals $p/q$ in the interval $(c - 1, c + 1)$ such that $0 < q \leq N$. There are only finitely many elements of the set $S_N$, and $c \notin S_N$ because $c$ is irrational. Thus the number

Strategy 3.1 cannot be used here, since there is no algebraic formula for $f(x)$.

$$\delta = \min\{|x - c| : x \in S_N\}$$

exists and is positive. Therefore the open interval $(c - \delta, c + \delta)$ contains *no* rationals $p/q$ with $0 < q \leq N$.

Hence if $|x - c| < \delta$, then

EITHER $x$ is irrational, so $f(x) = 0 < \varepsilon$,

OR $x = p/q$ with $q > N$, so $f(x) = 1/q < 1/N < \varepsilon$.

In either case $f(x) < \varepsilon$, so we have succeeded in choosing $\delta > 0$ such that statement (3.7) holds. Hence $f$ is continuous at $c$. ■

*Remark* In view of the strange continuity properties of the Riemann function, it is natural to ask whether a function can be found which is continuous at each rational point of $\mathbb{R}$ and discontinuous at each irrational point. However, it can be proved that no such function exists.

## Blancmange function

Our next function is in some ways even stranger than the Dirichlet and the Riemann functions. To construct this function, we start with the **sawtooth function** (illustrated in the margin):

$$s(x) = \begin{cases} x - [x], & \text{if } 0 \le x - [x] \le \frac{1}{2}, \\ 1 - (x - [x]), & \text{if } \frac{1}{2} < x - [x] < 1, \end{cases}$$

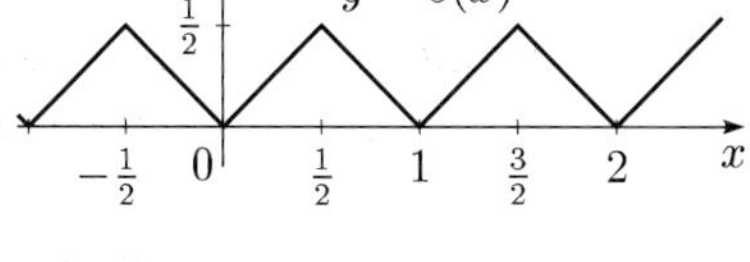


where $[x]$ is the integer part function.

The **blancmange function** $B$ is obtained by forming an infinite series of functions related to $s$:

$$B(x) = s(x) + \tfrac{1}{2}s(2x) + \tfrac{1}{4}s(4x) + \tfrac{1}{8}s(8x) + \cdots$$
$$= \sum_{n=0}^{\infty} \frac{1}{2^n} s(2^n x).$$

The strange properties of this function were first studied by the Japanese mathematician Teiji Takagi in 1903. The name 'blancmange function' was used by the English mathematician David Tall in the 1980s.

For example, to evaluate $B(\frac{1}{4})$ we find the sum of the corresponding series:

$$B(\tfrac{1}{4}) = s(\tfrac{1}{4}) + \tfrac{1}{2}s(\tfrac{1}{2}) + \tfrac{1}{4}s(1) + \tfrac{1}{8}s(2) + \cdots$$
$$= \tfrac{1}{4} + \tfrac{1}{2} \times \tfrac{1}{2} + \tfrac{1}{4} \times 0 + \tfrac{1}{8} \times 0 + \cdots$$
$$= \tfrac{1}{2}.$$

In this case, the series has only finitely many non-zero terms, but for some $x$ the series for $B(x)$ has infinitely many non-zero terms. However, since $0 \le s(x) \le \frac{1}{2}$, for $x \in \mathbb{R}$, we have

$$0 \le \frac{1}{2^n} s(2^n x) \le \frac{1}{2^{n+1}}, \quad \text{for } x \in \mathbb{R} \text{ and } n \in \mathbb{N},$$

so the series defining $B(x)$ is convergent for each $x \in \mathbb{R}$, by the Comparison Test for series.

See Unit AA3, Section 2.

To picture the graph of the blancmange function, we consider the graphs of several successive partial sum functions of the series for $B$, with domains restricted to $[0, 1]$. (In each case the graph of the previous partial sum function is in light dashes and the function being added is in heavy dashes.)

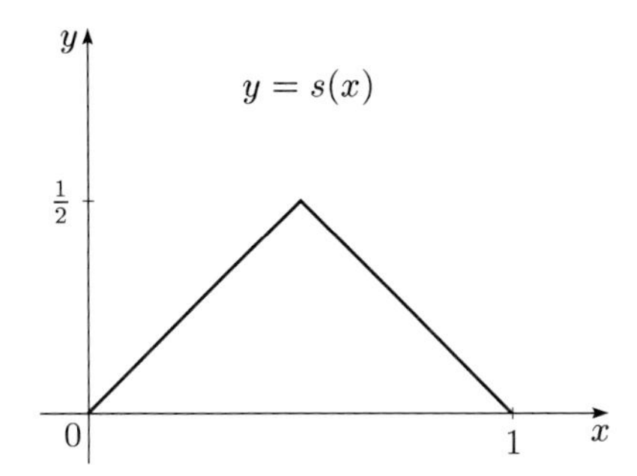


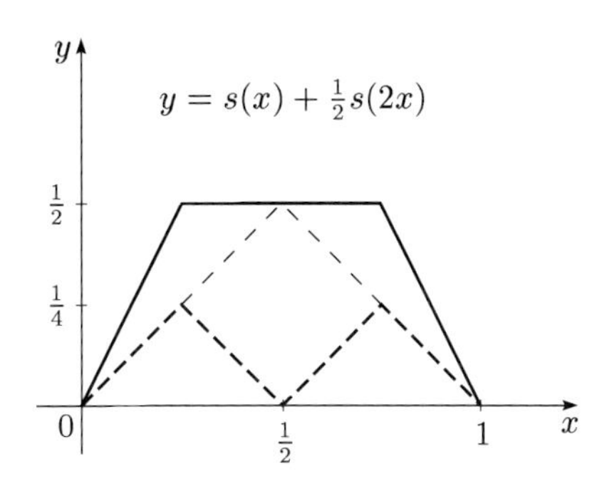


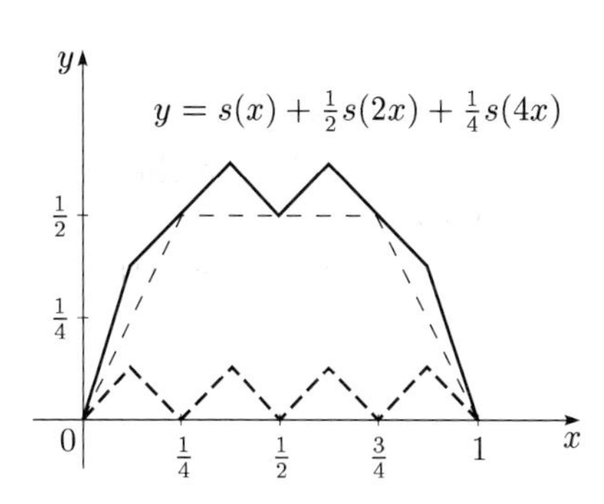

The sum function $B$ has the following graph.

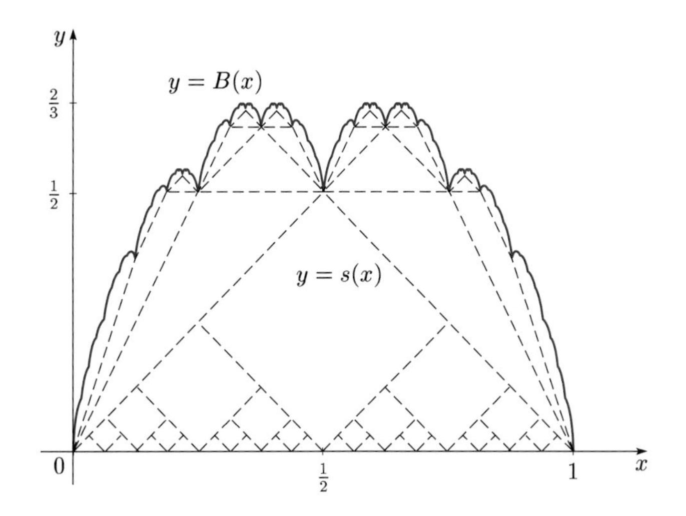


The dashes show the partial sum functions and the functions in the series for $B$.

The graph of $B$ is very irregular, in the sense that it oscillates rapidly up and down, and does not appear to be smooth at any point. However, it does seem that the function $B$ is continuous, and we can show that this is true.

In Unit AB2, you will see that the function $B$ is nowhere differentiable!

> **Theorem 3.4** The blancmange function is continuous.

**Proof** Let $c \in \mathbb{R}$. We want to show that

for each $\varepsilon > 0$, there exists $\delta > 0$ such that

$$|B(x) - B(c)| < \varepsilon, \quad \text{for all } x \text{ with } |x - c| < \delta. \tag{3.8}$$

If you are short of time, omit this proof.

Let $\varepsilon > 0$ be given. We first write

$$B(x) - B(c) = \sum_{n=0}^{\infty} \frac{1}{2^n} \left( s(2^n x) - s(2^n c) \right).$$

Hence, by the infinite form of the Triangle Inequality,

See Unit AA3, Section 3.

$$|B(x) - B(c)| \leq \sum_{n=0}^{\infty} \frac{1}{2^n} |s(2^n x) - s(2^n c)|. \tag{3.9}$$

For all $x$ and $c$, and $n = 0, 1, 2, \ldots$, both $s(2^n x)$ and $s(2^n c)$ lie in $[0, \frac{1}{2}]$, so

$$|s(2^n x) - s(2^n c)| \leq \tfrac{1}{2}, \quad \text{for } n = 0, 1, 2, \ldots. \tag{3.10}$$

Now we choose an integer $N$ such that $1/2^N < \frac{1}{2}\varepsilon$ and consider the series in inequality (3.9), starting from the term $n = N$. By inequality (3.10), we have

Such an $N$ exists because $\{1/2^n\}$ is a basic null sequence.

$$\begin{aligned} \sum_{n=N}^{\infty} \frac{1}{2^n} |s(2^n x) - s(2^n c)| &\leq \frac{1}{2} \sum_{n=N}^{\infty} \frac{1}{2^n} \\ &= \frac{1}{2} \left( \frac{1/2^N}{1 - 1/2} \right) = \frac{1}{2^N} < \tfrac{1}{2}\varepsilon. \end{aligned} \tag{3.11}$$

We have

$$\frac{1}{2^N} + \frac{1}{2^{N+1}} + \cdots = \frac{1/2^N}{1 - 1/2}.$$

Next we consider the rest of this series. Each of the functions

$$x \longmapsto s(2^n x), \quad n = 0, 1, \ldots, N - 1,$$

is continuous.

Therefore, for each $n = 0, 1, \ldots, N-1$, there is a positive number $\delta_n$ such that

$$|s(2^n x) - s(2^n c)| < \tfrac{1}{4}\varepsilon, \quad \text{for all } x \text{ with } |x - c| < \delta_n.$$

Thus if $\delta = \min\{\delta_0, \delta_1, \ldots, \delta_{N-1}\}$ and $|x - c| < \delta$, then

$$\sum_{n=0}^{N-1} \frac{1}{2^n}|s(2^n x) - s(2^n c)| < \sum_{n=0}^{N-1} \frac{1}{2^n}\left(\tfrac{1}{4}\varepsilon\right) < 2 \times \tfrac{1}{4}\varepsilon = \tfrac{1}{2}\varepsilon.$$

We have $\displaystyle\sum_{n=0}^{\infty} \frac{1}{2^n} = 2.$

Combining this inequality with inequalities (3.11) and (3.9), we obtain statement (3.8) with this choice of $\delta$. Hence $B$ is continuous at the point $c$. ■

The blancmange function is very irregular, but it exhibits patterns known as 'self-similarity'. However closely you look at the graph, you can see 'mini-blancmanges' growing on it everywhere. The existence of these mini-blancmanges can be explained by rewriting the series defining $B$:

$$\begin{aligned} B(x) &= s(x) + \tfrac{1}{2}s(2x) + \tfrac{1}{4}s(4x) + \tfrac{1}{8}s(8x) + \cdots \\ &= s(x) + \tfrac{1}{2}\left(s(2x) + \tfrac{1}{2}s(4x) + \tfrac{1}{4}s(8x) + \cdots\right) \\ &= s(x) + \tfrac{1}{2}B(2x). \end{aligned}$$

The graph of the function $x \longmapsto \frac{1}{2}B(2x)$ is just the graph of $B$ scaled by the factor $\frac{1}{2}$ in both $x$- and $y$-directions. Hence the graph of $B$ is the graph of $s$ with a (sheared) $\frac{1}{2}$-size blancmange growing on each sloping line segment. Smaller mini-blancmanges can be explained in a similar manner.

See Unit LA4, Section 1, for details about shears.

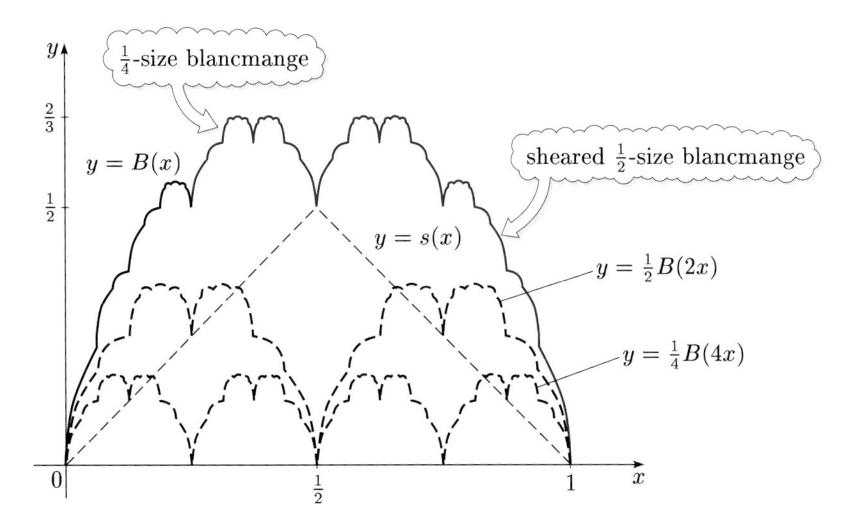


Such irregular sets, which display self-similarity, are studied in detail in the subject known as 'fractals'.

## 3.3 Limits and other asymptotic behaviour

In Sections 1 and 2 we defined limits and other types of asymptotic behaviour using a sequential approach. Each of these concepts can also be defined in a way that is analogous to the $\varepsilon$–$\delta$ definition of continuity. For example, we can define the concept of a limit as follows.

> **Definition** Let $f$ be a function defined on a punctured neighbourhood $N_r(c)$ of $c$. Then $f(x)$ **tends to the limit $l$ as $x$ tends to $c$** if
>
> for each $\varepsilon > 0$, there exists $\delta > 0$ such that
> $$|f(x) - l| < \varepsilon, \quad \text{for all } x \text{ with } 0 < |x - c| < \delta.$$
> As before, we write
> $$\lim_{x \to c} f(x) = l \quad \text{or} \quad f(x) \to l \text{ as } x \to c.$$

*Remarks*

1. This definition is very similar to the $\varepsilon$–$\delta$ definition of continuity, except that $f(c)$ is replaced by $l$ and $|x - c| < \delta$ is replaced by $0 < |x - c| < \delta$. This reflects the fact that when we try to find the limit of $f(x)$ at $c$, the value $f(c)$ is not relevant and may not be defined.

The proof that the above definition is equivalent to the sequential definition of a limit is similar to the proof of Theorem 3.1.

2. There are analogous definitions of the following concepts:
$$\lim_{x \to c^+} f(x) = l, \qquad \lim_{x \to c^-} f(x) = l;$$
$$\lim_{x \to \infty} f(x) = l, \qquad \lim_{x \to -\infty} f(x) = l;$$
$$f(x) \to \infty \text{ as } x \to c, \qquad f(x) \to \infty \text{ as } x \to c^+ \text{ (or } c^-\text{)};$$
$$f(x) \to \infty \text{ as } x \to \infty, \qquad f(x) \to \infty \text{ as } x \to -\infty.$$
For example, $\lim_{x \to \infty} f(x) = l$ if

for each $\varepsilon > 0$, there exists $K \in \mathbb{R}$ such that
$$|f(x) - l| < \varepsilon, \quad \text{for all } x \text{ with } x > K.$$

Here is an example of a limit evaluated using the $\varepsilon$–$\delta$ definition.

However, in this example, the sequential definition is easier to use; see Example 1.1(a).

**Example 3.2** Use the $\varepsilon$–$\delta$ definition of a limit to evaluate
$$\lim_{x \to 2} \frac{x^2 - 4}{x - 2}.$$

**Solution** The domain of $f(x) = (x^2 - 4)/(x - 2)$ is $\mathbb{R} - \{2\}$, so $f$ is defined on each punctured neighbourhood of 2. Also,
$$f(x) = \frac{x^2 - 4}{x - 2} = \frac{(x - 2)(x + 2)}{x - 2} = x + 2, \quad \text{for } x \neq 2.$$
This formula suggests that $\lim_{x \to 2} f(x) = 2 + 2 = 4$, so we must prove that

for each $\varepsilon > 0$, there exists $\delta > 0$ such that
$$|f(x) - 4| < \varepsilon, \quad \text{for all } x \text{ with } 0 < |x - 2| < \delta.$$

But $|f(x) - 4| = |x + 2 - 4| = |x - 2|$, for $x \neq 2$, so the above statement is true if we choose $\delta = \varepsilon$. Hence
$$\lim_{x \to 2} \frac{x^2 - 4}{x - 2} = 4. \quad \blacksquare$$

This is similar to a proof, using Strategy 3.1, that the function $x \longmapsto x + 2$ is continuous at the point 2.

**Exercise 3.2** Use the $\varepsilon$–$\delta$ definition of a limit to evaluate
$$\lim_{x \to 1} \frac{2x^3 + 3x - 5}{x - 1}.$$
Hint: Use the fact that $2x^3 + 3x - 5 = (x - 1)(2x^2 + 2x + 5)$ and follow Strategy 3.1 for using the $\varepsilon$–$\delta$ definition of continuity.

## Further exercises

**Exercise 3.3** Use the $\varepsilon$–$\delta$ definition to prove that each of the following functions $f$ is continuous at the given point $c$:

(a) $f(x) = 6x^2 - x, \quad c = -1;$

(b) $f(x) = x^5, \quad c = 0;$

(c) $f(x) = \sqrt{x}, \quad c = 4;$

(d) $f(x) = \dfrac{1}{x}, \quad c = 1.$

Hint: In part (c), use the fact that $(\sqrt{x} - 2)(\sqrt{x} + 2) = x - 4$.

**Exercise 3.4** Use the $\varepsilon$–$\delta$ definition to evaluate

$$\lim_{x \to -1} \frac{x^3 + 1}{x + 1}.$$

# 4 Uniform continuity

After working through this section, you should be able to:

(a) understand the definition of *uniform continuity* and use it in simple cases;

(b) know and use various conditions for uniform continuity.

In Section 3 we described an alternative approach to continuity, based on the $\varepsilon$–$\delta$ definition. In this section we use this approach to describe a stronger notion of continuity, which plays a key role in our later work on the integration of continuous functions.

See Unit AB3, Section 1.

## 4.1 What is uniform continuity?

The $\varepsilon$–$\delta$ definition of continuity states that a function $f$ is continuous at a point $c$ in the domain $A$ of $f$ if

for each $\varepsilon > 0$, there exists $\delta > 0$ such that

$$|f(x) - f(c)| < \varepsilon, \quad \text{for all } x \in A \text{ with } |x - c| < \delta.$$

In this definition we cannot expect that, for a given positive number $\varepsilon$, the same positive number $\delta$ will serve equally well for each point $c$ in $A$. Sometimes, however, this does happen, in which case:

for each $\varepsilon > 0$, there exists $\delta > 0$ such that

$$|f(x) - f(c)| < \varepsilon, \quad \text{for all } x, c \in A \text{ with } |x - c| < \delta.$$

We make the following definition.

**Definition** A function $f$ defined on an interval $I$ is **uniformly continuous** on $I$ if

for each $\varepsilon > 0$, there exists $\delta > 0$ such that

$$|f(x) - f(y)| < \varepsilon, \quad \text{for all } x, y \in I \text{ with } |x - y| < \delta. \qquad (4.1)$$

In this definition, we have used the variables $x$ and $y$, rather than $x$ and $c$, to indicate that these two variables are of equal standing.

*Remarks*

1. We say that $c$ is an **interior point** of an interval $I$ if $c$ is not an endpoint of $I$. It follows from the above definition that if $f$ is uniformly continuous on an interval $I$, then $f$ is continuous at each interior point of $I$.

At an endpoint of $I$, the function can be discontinuous because of its behaviour *outside* $I$.

2. Also, if $f$ is uniformly continuous on an interval $I$, then $f$ is uniformly continuous on any subinterval of $I$.

**Example 4.1** Prove from the definition that $f(x) = x^2$ is uniformly continuous on $I = [-4, 4]$.

In Exercise 4.1(b), you will see that $f(x) = x^2$ is not uniformly continuous on $\mathbb{R}$.

**Solution** Let $\varepsilon > 0$ be given. We have

$$f(x) - f(y) = x^2 - y^2 = (x + y)(x - y).$$

Hence, for $x, y \in [-4, 4]$,

$$\begin{aligned} |f(x) - f(y)| &= |x + y|\,|x - y| \\ &\leq (|x| + |y|)|x - y| \quad \text{(Triangle Inequality)} \\ &\leq 8|x - y|, \end{aligned}$$

since $|x| \leq 4$ and $|y| \leq 4$.

Thus, if we choose $\delta = \frac{1}{8}\varepsilon$, then whenever $x, y \in [-4, 4]$ and $|x - y| < \delta$, we have

$$\begin{aligned} |f(x) - f(y)| &\leq 8|x - y| \\ &< 8 \times \tfrac{1}{8}\varepsilon = \varepsilon. \end{aligned}$$

Hence $f$ is uniformly continuous on $[-4, 4]$. ■

The next example shows that a function can be continuous on an interval but not uniformly continuous on that interval.

**Example 4.2** Prove that $f(x) = 1/x$ is not uniformly continuous on $I = (0, 1]$.

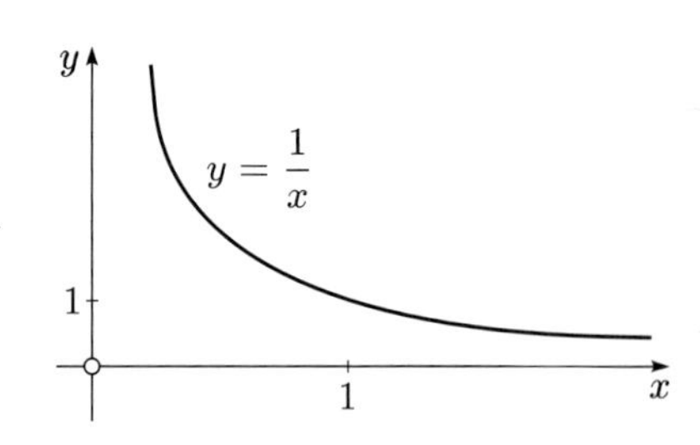


**Solution** We have to find $\varepsilon > 0$ such that, no matter which $\delta > 0$ is chosen, there are points $x$ and $y$ in $I$ with $|x - y| < \delta$ and $|f(x) - f(y)| \geq \varepsilon$.

The graph suggests that, for any positive $\delta$, we should take $x$ and $y$ near 0 because then $x$ and $y$ are close together but $f(x)$ and $f(y)$ can be far apart. We try $x = \frac{1}{2}\delta$ and $y = \delta$, where $0 < \delta < 1$. Then

$$|x - y| = |\tfrac{1}{2}\delta - \delta| = \tfrac{1}{2}\delta < \delta$$

and

$$|f(x) - f(y)| = \left| \frac{1}{\frac{1}{2}\delta} - \frac{1}{\delta} \right| = \frac{2}{\delta} - \frac{1}{\delta} = \frac{1}{\delta} > 1.$$

Hence the definition fails with $\varepsilon = 1$, so $f$ is not uniformly continuous on $I$. ■

The reasoning in this solution is quite subtle and can be tricky to apply, so it is useful to reformulate what it means to say that a function is *not* uniformly continuous on an interval. Roughly speaking, this happens if you can find pairs of points in the interval, as close together as you like, whose images are not close together.

**Theorem 4.1** Let the function $f$ be defined on an interval $I$. Then $f$ is not uniformly continuous on $I$ if and only if there exist two sequences $\{x_n\}$ and $\{y_n\}$ in $I$, and $\varepsilon > 0$, such that

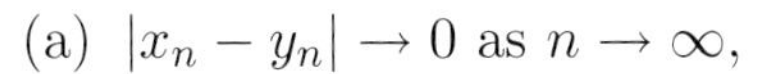

(a) $|x_n - y_n| \to 0$ as $n \to \infty$,

(b) $|f(x_n) - f(y_n)| \geq \varepsilon$, for $n = 1, 2, \ldots$.

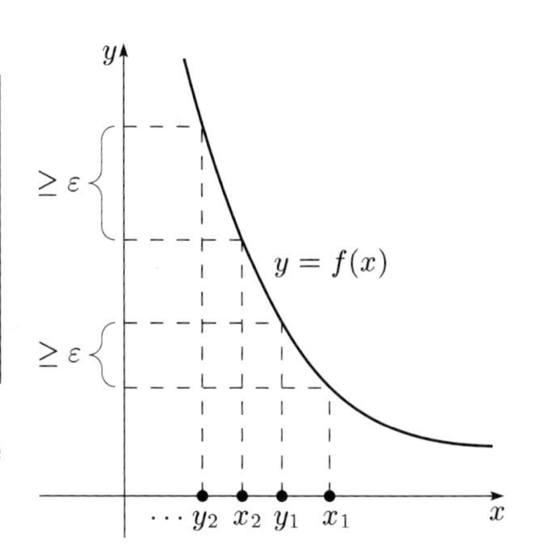


**Proof** First suppose that $f$ is not uniformly continuous on $I$. Then there exists $\varepsilon > 0$ such that for all $\delta > 0$ there are points $x$ and $y$ in $I$ with

$$|x - y| < \delta \quad \text{and} \quad |f(x) - f(y)| \geq \varepsilon.$$

Applying this fact with $\delta = 1$, $\delta = \frac{1}{2}$, $\delta = \frac{1}{3}$, and so on, we obtain sequences $\{x_n\}$ and $\{y_n\}$ in $I$ such that

$$|x_n - y_n| < \frac{1}{n} \quad \text{and} \quad |f(x_n) - f(y_n)| \geq \varepsilon, \quad \text{for } n = 1, 2, \ldots.$$

Thus statements (a) and (b) both hold.

On the other hand, suppose that there exist sequences $\{x_n\}$ and $\{y_n\}$ in $I$, and $\varepsilon > 0$, such that statements (a) and (b) hold. If $f$ *is* uniformly continuous on $I$, then there exists $\delta > 0$ such that

This is a proof by contradiction.

$$|f(x) - f(y)| < \varepsilon, \quad \text{for all } x, y \in I \text{ with } |x - y| < \delta.$$

But $|x_n - y_n| < \delta$, for $n > N$ say, by statement (a), so

$$|f(x_n) - f(y_n)| < \varepsilon, \quad \text{for } n > N,$$

contradicting statement (b). Thus $f$ is not uniformly continuous on $I$. ■

Theorem 4.1 gives us the second part of the following strategy; the first part is an elaboration of the definition.

**Strategy 4.1** To check uniform continuity.

Let the function $f$ be defined on an interval $I$.

1. To prove that $f$ is uniformly continuous on $I$, find an expression for $\delta > 0$ in terms of a given $\varepsilon > 0$ such that

$$|f(x) - f(y)| < \varepsilon, \quad \text{for all } x, y \in I \text{ with } |x - y| < \delta.$$

2. To prove that $f$ is not uniformly continuous on $I$, find two sequences $\{x_n\}$ and $\{y_n\}$ in $I$, and $\varepsilon > 0$, such that

$$|x_n - y_n| \to 0 \text{ as } n \to \infty,$$
$$|f(x_n) - f(y_n)| \geq \varepsilon, \quad \text{for } n = 1, 2, \ldots.$$

In part 2, you should aim to choose the terms $x_n$ and $y_n$ close together at points of $I$ where the graph of $f$ is steep; see Exercise 4.1(b), for example.

In Example 4.2, we could have applied part 2 of this strategy, by taking $x_n = 1/(2n)$ and $y_n = 1/n$, $n = 1, 2, \ldots$, since $\{x_n\}$ and $\{y_n\}$ lie in $I$,

$$|x_n - y_n| = \left|\frac{1}{2n} - \frac{1}{n}\right| = \frac{1}{2n} \to 0 \text{ as } n \to \infty$$

and, for $n = 1, 2, \ldots$,

$$|f(x_n) - f(y_n)| = \left|\frac{1}{x_n} - \frac{1}{y_n}\right| = \left|\frac{1}{1/(2n)} - \frac{1}{1/n}\right| = n \geq 1,$$

so part 2 applies with $\varepsilon = 1$.

Try the next exercise using Strategy 4.1.

**Exercise 4.1**

(a) Prove that $f(x) = x^3$ is uniformly continuous on $I = [-2, 2]$.

(b) Prove that $f(x) = x^2$ is not uniformly continuous on $I = \mathbb{R}$.

Hint: Take $x_n = n + 1/n$ and $y_n = n$, $n = 1, 2, \ldots$.

## 4.2 A sufficient condition for uniform continuity

Checking uniform continuity from the definition can be complicated. However, we can often deduce uniform continuity in a straightforward way from the following fundamental result. This is another illustration, like the Intermediate Value Theorem and the Extreme Value Theorem, of the fact that continuous functions on bounded closed intervals have particularly good properties.

See Unit AA4, Section 3.

> **Theorem 4.2** If the function $f$ is continuous on a bounded closed interval $[a, b]$, then $f$ is uniformly continuous on $[a, b]$.

The uniform continuity of the function $f(x) = x^2$ on $[-4, 4]$ can be deduced immediately from Theorem 4.2, as follows. The function $f(x) = x^2$ is continuous on the whole of $\mathbb{R}$, so it must be uniformly continuous on *any* bounded closed interval, by Theorem 4.2. However, $f(x) = x^2$ is not uniformly continuous on the set $\mathbb{R}$, as you saw in Exercise 4.1(b).

See Example 4.1.

**Exercise 4.2** Use Theorem 4.2 to prove that $f(x) = x^3$ is uniformly continuous on $I = [-2, 2]$.

### Proof of Theorem 4.2

We assume that $f$ is continuous on $[a, b]$ but not uniformly continuous on $[a, b]$, and deduce a contradiction using the bisection method.

If you are short of time, omit this proof.

Since $f$ is not uniformly continuous on $[a, b]$, there exist, by Theorem 4.1, sequences $\{x_n\}$ and $\{y_n\}$ in $[a, b]$, and $\varepsilon > 0$, such that

The bisection method was introduced in Unit AA4, Section 3.

$$|x_n - y_n| \to 0 \quad \text{as } n \to \infty, \qquad (4.2)$$

$$|f(x_n) - f(y_n)| \geq \varepsilon, \quad \text{for } n = 1, 2, \ldots. \qquad (4.3)$$

Let $a_0 = a$, $b_0 = b$ and $p = \frac{1}{2}(a_0 + b_0)$. One of $[a_0, p]$ or $[p, b_0]$ must contain terms $x_n$ for infinitely many $n \in \mathbb{N}$. We denote this interval by $[a_1, b_1]$. Thus:

1. $[a_1, b_1] \subseteq [a_0, b_0]$;
2. $b_1 - a_1 = \frac{1}{2}(b_0 - a_0)$;
3. $[a_1, b_1]$ contains terms $x_n$ for infinitely many $n \in \mathbb{N}$.

Now we repeat this process, bisecting $[a_1, b_1]$ to obtain $[a_2, b_2]$, and so on. This gives a sequence of closed intervals

$$[a_k, b_k], \quad k = 0, 1, 2, \ldots,$$

We use $k$ here to avoid $n$ having two meanings.

such that the following properties hold:

1. $[a_{k+1}, b_{k+1}] \subseteq [a_k, b_k]$, for $k = 0, 1, 2, \ldots$;
2. $b_k - a_k = (\frac{1}{2})^k (b_0 - a_0)$, for $k = 0, 1, 2, \ldots$;
3. $[a_k, b_k]$ contains terms $x_n$ for infinitely many $n \in \mathbb{N}$.

Property 1 implies that $\{a_k\}$ is increasing and bounded above by $b_0$. Hence, by the Monotone Convergence Theorem, $\{a_k\}$ is convergent. Let

See Unit AA2, Theorem 5.1.

$$\lim_{k\to\infty} a_k = c;$$

then, by property 2 and the Combination Rules for sequences, $\lim\limits_{k\to\infty} b_k = c$ also.

By property 3, the sequence $\{x_n\}$ contains a subsequence $\{x_{n_k}\}$ such that

$$x_{n_k} \in [a_k, b_k], \quad \text{for } k = 0, 1, 2, \ldots.$$

Thus $\lim\limits_{k\to\infty} x_{n_k} = c$, by the Squeeze Rule for sequences, so

$$y_{n_k} = (y_{n_k} - x_{n_k}) + x_{n_k} \to 0 + c = c,$$

by statement (4.2). It follows from the continuity of $f$ at the point $c$ that

$$\lim_{k\to\infty} f(x_{n_k}) = f(c) \quad \text{and} \quad \lim_{k\to\infty} f(y_{n_k}) = f(c),$$

but this contradicts statement (4.3). This completes the proof. ■

As part of this proof, we showed that any sequence $\{x_n\}$ in $[a, b]$ contains a convergent subsequence $\{x_{n_k}\}$. This remarkable result, which is of importance in many parts of analysis, is called the *Bolzano–Weierstrass Theorem*. It can be stated as follows.

Bernard Bolzano (1781–1848) was a Czech theologian, philosopher and mathematician whose pioneering work in analysis was not recognised until after his death.

Karl Weierstrass (1815–1897) was a German mathematician who made many major contributions to analysis. His lectures in Berlin form the basis of what is now a 'course on analysis'.

**Theorem 4.3 Bolzano–Weierstrass Theorem**

Any bounded sequence has a convergent subsequence.

## Further exercises

**Exercise 4.3** Use Strategy 4.1 to determine whether each of the following functions is uniformly continuous on the given interval:

(a) $f(x) = x, \quad I = \mathbb{R}$;

(b) $f(x) = \dfrac{1}{x^2}, \quad I = (0, 3]$;

(c) $f(x) = \dfrac{2x}{1+x}, \quad I = [0, \infty)$;

(d) $f(x) = e^x, \quad I = \mathbb{R}$.

**Exercise 4.4** Use Theorem 4.2 to prove that the function in Exercise 4.3(c) is uniformly continuous on the interval $[-\frac{1}{2}, 0]$.

# Solutions to the exercises

**1.1** **(a)** The function

$$f(x) = \frac{x^2 + x}{x}$$

has domain $\mathbb{R} - \{0\}$, so $f$ is defined on any punctured neighbourhood of 0. Also,

$$f(x) = \frac{x(x+1)}{x} = x + 1, \quad \text{for } x \neq 0.$$

Thus if $\{x_n\}$ lies in $\mathbb{R} - \{0\}$ and $x_n \to 0$, then

$$f(x_n) = x_n + 1 \to 1.$$

Hence

$$\lim_{x \to 0} \frac{x^2 + x}{x} = 1.$$

**(b)** The domain of $f(x) = [x]$ is $\mathbb{R}$, so $f$ is defined on any punctured neighbourhood of 1. Now,

$$f(x) = 0, \quad \text{for } 0 \le x < 1,$$

and

$$f(x) = 1, \quad \text{for } 1 \le x < 2.$$

The two sequences $\{1 + 1/n\}$ and $\{1 - 1/n\}$ both tend to 1, and have terms lying in $\mathbb{R} - \{1\}$. Also,

$$\lim_{n \to \infty} f(1 + 1/n) = 1 \quad \text{but} \quad \lim_{n \to \infty} f(1 - 1/n) = 0.$$

Hence $\lim_{x \to 1} [x]$ does not exist.

**(c)** The function $f(x) = \log_e |x|$ has domain $\mathbb{R} - \{0\}$, so it is defined in any punctured neighbourhood of 0, and its graph is as follows.

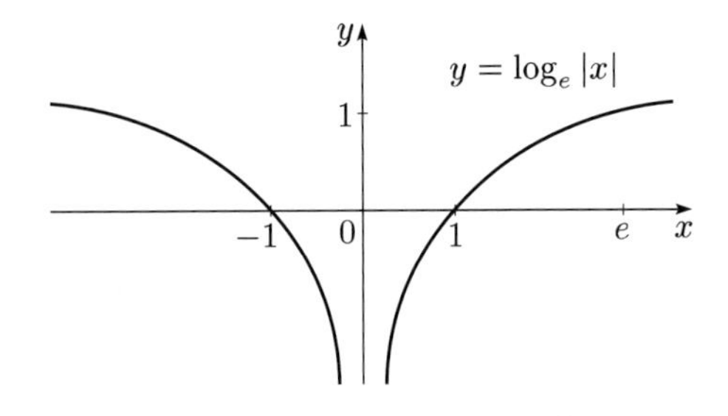


We consider the null sequence $x_n = 1/n$. Then

$$f(x_n) = \log_e |x_n| = \log_e(1/n) = -\log_e n.$$

Now $\log_e n \to \infty$ as $n \to \infty$, so $f(x_n) \to -\infty$ as $n \to \infty$.

Hence $\lim_{x \to 0} \log_e |x|$ does not exist.

**1.2** **(a)** The continuous function $f(x) = \sqrt{x}$ has domain the interval $[0, \infty)$, so it is defined on the open interval $(0, \infty)$, which contains 2. Hence, by Theorem 1.2, we have

$$\lim_{x \to 2} \sqrt{x} = \sqrt{2}.$$

**(b)** Since $\sin x > 0$ for $0 < x < \pi$, the function $f(x) = \sqrt{\sin x}$ is defined on the open interval $(0, \pi)$, which contains $\pi/2$, and is continuous, by the Composition Rule for continuous functions. Hence, by Theorem 1.2, we have

$$\lim_{x \to \pi/2} \sqrt{\sin x} = \sqrt{\sin(\pi/2)} = 1.$$

**(c)** The function $f(x) = e^x/(1 + x)$ is defined on the open interval $(-1, \infty)$, which contains 1, and is continuous, by the Quotient Rule for continuous functions. Hence, by Theorem 1.2, we have

$$\lim_{x \to 1} \frac{e^x}{1 + x} = \frac{e^1}{1 + 1} = \tfrac{1}{2}e.$$

**1.3** **(a)** First we write

$$\frac{\sin x}{2x + x^2} = \frac{\sin x}{x(2 + x)} = \left(\frac{\sin x}{x}\right)\left(\frac{1}{2 + x}\right).$$

Since

$$\lim_{x \to 0} \frac{\sin x}{x} = 1 \quad \text{(Theorem 1.1)}$$

and

$$\lim_{x \to 0} \frac{1}{2 + x} = \tfrac{1}{2} \quad \text{(Theorem 1.2)},$$

we deduce, by the Product Rule for limits, that

$$\lim_{x \to 0} \frac{\sin x}{2x + x^2} = 1 \times \tfrac{1}{2} = \tfrac{1}{2}.$$

**(b)** We can write

$$\frac{\sin(\sin x)}{\sin x} = g(f(x)),$$

where $f(x) = \sin x$ and $g(x) = \dfrac{\sin x}{x}$.

Substituting $u = f(x) = \sin x$, we have

$$u = \sin x \to 0 \quad \text{as } x \to 0,$$

$$g(u) = \frac{\sin u}{u} \to 1 \quad \text{as } u \to 0.$$

Thus, by the Composition Rule,

$$g(f(x)) = \frac{\sin(\sin x)}{\sin x} \to 1 \quad \text{as } x \to 0.$$

**(c)** We can write

$$\left(\frac{x}{\sin x}\right)^{1/2} = g(f(x)),$$

where $f(x) = \dfrac{\sin x}{x}$ and $g(x) = 1/x^{1/2}$.

Substituting $u = f(x) = \dfrac{\sin x}{x}$, we have

$$u = \frac{\sin x}{x} \to 1 \quad \text{as } x \to 0,$$

$$g(u) = 1/u^{1/2} \to 1/1^{1/2} = 1 \quad \text{as } u \to 1.$$

Thus, by the Composition Rule,

$$g(f(x)) = \left(\frac{x}{\sin x}\right)^{1/2} \to 1 \quad \text{as } x \to 0.$$

**1.4** (a) Since

$$1 + x \le e^x \le \frac{1}{1-x}, \quad \text{for } |x| < 1,$$

we have

$$x \le e^x - 1 \le \frac{1}{1-x} - 1 = \frac{x}{1-x}, \quad \text{for } |x| < 1.$$

Hence

$$1 \le \frac{e^x - 1}{x} \le \frac{1}{1-x} = 1 + \frac{x}{1-x}, \quad \text{for } 0 < x < 1,$$

and

$$1 \ge \frac{e^x - 1}{x} \ge \frac{1}{1-x} = 1 + \frac{x}{1-x}, \quad \text{for } -1 < x < 0.$$

Since $x = -|x|$, for $x < 0$, and $1 - x > 0$, for $|x| < 1$, we deduce that

$$1 - \frac{|x|}{1-x} \le \frac{e^x - 1}{x} \le 1 + \frac{|x|}{1-x}, \quad \text{for } |x| < 1,$$

as required.

(b) We have

$$\lim_{x \to 0} 1 - \frac{|x|}{1-x} = 1 \quad \text{and} \quad \lim_{x \to 0} 1 + \frac{|x|}{1-x} = 1,$$

because both functions are continuous on the interval $(-1, 1)$.

Thus, by part (a) and the Squeeze Rule,

$$\lim_{x \to 0} \frac{e^x - 1}{x} = 1.$$

**1.5** (a) Since $\lim_{x \to 0} \frac{\sin x}{x} = 1$ and the function $x \longmapsto \sqrt{x}$ is continuous at 0, we have

$$\lim_{x \to 0^+} \frac{\sin x}{x} = 1 \quad \text{(Theorem 1.4)}$$

and

$$\lim_{x \to 0^+} \sqrt{x} = 0 \quad \text{(Theorem 1.5)}.$$

Hence, by the Sum Rule,

$$\lim_{x \to 0^+} \left( \frac{\sin x}{x} + \sqrt{x} \right) = 1 + 0 = 1.$$

(b) We can write

$$\frac{\sin \sqrt{x}}{\sqrt{x}} = g(f(x)),$$

where $f(x) = \sqrt{x}$ and $g(x) = \dfrac{\sin x}{x}$.

Substituting $u = f(x) = \sqrt{x}$, we have

$$u = \sqrt{x} \to 0 \quad \text{as } x \to 0^+,$$

$$g(u) = \frac{\sin u}{u} \to 1 \quad \text{as } u \to 0.$$

Thus, by the one-sided limit version of the Composition Rule,

$$g(f(x)) = \frac{\sin \sqrt{x}}{\sqrt{x}} \to 1 \quad \text{as } x \to 0^+.$$

**1.6** (a) The domain of $f$ is $\mathbb{R} - \{1\}$, so $f$ is defined on each punctured neighbourhood of 1. Also,

$$f(x) = \frac{x^3 - 1}{x - 1} = \frac{(x-1)(x^2 + x + 1)}{x - 1} = x^2 + x + 1, \quad \text{for } x \ne 1.$$

Thus if $\{x_n\}$ is any sequence in $\mathbb{R} - \{1\}$ such that $x_n \to 1$, then

$$f(x_n) = x_n^2 + x_n + 1 \to 1 + 1 + 1 = 3 \quad \text{as } n \to \infty,$$

by the Combination Rules for sequences. Hence

$$\lim_{x \to 1} \frac{x^3 - 1}{x - 1} = 3.$$

(b) The presence of the modulus in the denominator of

$$f(x) = \frac{x^3 - 1}{|x - 1|}$$

suggests that the limit of $f(x)$ as $x$ tends to 1 does not exist, because the quotient may behave in a different way on either side of 1.

Therefore we consider the two sequences

$$x_n = 1 + 1/n, \quad y_n = 1 - 1/n, \quad n = 1, 2, \ldots.$$

Both sequences tend to 1 from within $\mathbb{R} - \{1\}$, but

$$\begin{aligned} f(x_n) &= \frac{(1 + 1/n)^3 - 1}{|(1 + 1/n) - 1|} \\ &= \frac{(1 + 3/n + 3/n^2 + 1/n^3) - 1}{1/n} \\ &= 3 + 3/n + 1/n^2 \to 3, \end{aligned}$$

whereas

$$\begin{aligned} f(y_n) &= \frac{(1 - 1/n)^3 - 1}{|(1 - 1/n) - 1|} \\ &= \frac{(1 - 3/n + 3/n^2 - 1/n^3) - 1}{1/n} \\ &= -3 + 3/n - 1/n^2 \to -3. \end{aligned}$$

Hence

$$\lim_{x \to 1} \frac{x^3 - 1}{|x - 1|} \text{ does not exist.}$$

(c) The function $x \longmapsto e^{x^2}$ is defined and continuous on $\mathbb{R}$. Hence, by Theorem 1.2,

$$\lim_{x \to 2} e^{x^2} = e^4.$$

(d) The term $1/x^2$ is large near 0, so $\cos(1/x^2)$ is highly oscillatory for $x$ near 0. This suggests that this one-sided limit does not exist. Therefore we use the one-sided limit version of Strategy 1.1.

Consider the sequence

$$x_n = \frac{1}{\sqrt{2n\pi}}, \quad n = 1, 2, \ldots,$$

chosen because

$$\cos(1/x_n^2) = \cos(2n\pi) = 1, \quad \text{for } n = 1, 2, \ldots.$$

Then $x_n > 0$ and $x_n \to 0$, and

$$\begin{aligned} f(x_n) &= \frac{\cos(1/x_n^2)}{x_n} \\ &= \frac{\cos(2n\pi)}{1/\sqrt{2n\pi}} \\ &= \sqrt{2n\pi} \to \infty \quad \text{as } n \to \infty. \end{aligned}$$

Hence $f(x) = (\cos(1/x^2))/x$ does not tend to a limit as $x \to 0^+$.

**1.7** **(a)** The function $x \longmapsto \sin x$ is defined and continuous on $\mathbb{R}$. Hence, by Theorem 1.2,

$$\lim_{x\to 0} \sin x = \sin 0 = 0.$$

We also know that

$$\lim_{x\to 0} \frac{e^x - 1}{x} = 1;$$

see Theorem 1.3(c). Hence, by the Sum Rule,

$$\lim_{x\to 0} \left(\sin x + \frac{e^x - 1}{x}\right) = 0 + 1 = 1.$$

**(b)** Using the hint, we obtain

$$\frac{1-\cos x}{x} = \frac{2\sin^2(\frac{1}{2}x)}{x} = \frac{\sin(\frac{1}{2}x)}{\frac{1}{2}x} \times \sin(\tfrac{1}{2}x).$$

Now,

$$\lim_{x\to 0} \frac{\sin(\frac{1}{2}x)}{\frac{1}{2}x} = 1,$$

by Example 1.3(a), and

$$\lim_{x\to 0} \sin(\tfrac{1}{2}x) = 0,$$

by the continuity of the function $x \longmapsto \sin(\frac{1}{2}x)$.

Thus, by the Product Rule,

$$\lim_{x\to 0} \frac{1-\cos x}{x} = 1 \times 0 = 0.$$

**(c)** We can write

$$\frac{e^{|x|} - 1}{|x|} = g(f(x)),$$

where $f(x) = |x|$ and $g(x) = \dfrac{e^x - 1}{x}$.

Substituting $u = f(x) = |x|$, we have

$$u = |x| \to 0 \text{ as } x \to 0$$

(since the function $x \longmapsto |x|$ is continuous),

$$g(u) = \frac{e^u - 1}{u} \to 1 \text{ as } u \to 0.$$

Thus, by the Composition Rule,

$$g(f(x)) = \frac{e^{|x|} - 1}{|x|} \to 1 \text{ as } x \to 0.$$

**(d)** First, the function

$$f(x) = \frac{x^3 - 1}{|x - 1|}$$

is defined on $(-\infty, 1)$.

Next, for $x < 1$ we have $|x - 1| = 1 - x$, so

$$f(x) = \frac{x^3 - 1}{1 - x} = -(x^2 + x + 1), \quad \text{for } x < 1.$$

Thus if $\{x_n\}$ lies in $(-\infty, 1)$ and $x_n \to 1$, then

$$f(x_n) = -(x_n^2 + x_n + 1) \to -(1 + 1 + 1) = -3,$$

by the Combination Rules for sequences. Hence

$$\lim_{x\to 1^-} \frac{x^3 - 1}{|x - 1|} = -3.$$

**2.1** **(a)** Let $f(x) = |x|$; then $f(x) > 0$ for $x \in \mathbb{R} - \{0\}$, and

$$\lim_{x\to 0} |x| = 0,$$

since $f$ is continuous at 0. Hence, by the Reciprocal Rule,

$$\frac{1}{f(x)} = \frac{1}{|x|} \to \infty \text{ as } x \to 0.$$

**(b)** Let $f(x) = x^3/\sin x$; then

$$f(x) = \frac{x^2}{(\sin x)/x} > 0, \quad \text{for } x \in N_\pi(0),$$

and

$$f(x) = \frac{x^2}{(\sin x)/x} \to \frac{0}{1} = 0 \text{ as } x \to 0,$$

by Theorem 1.3(a) and the Quotient Rule, since the function $x \longmapsto x^2$ is continuous at 0.

Hence, by the Reciprocal Rule,

$$\frac{1}{f(x)} = \frac{\sin x}{x^3} \to \infty \text{ as } x \to 0.$$

**(c)** Let $f(x) = x^3 - 1$; then $f(x) > 0$ for $x \in (1, \infty)$, and

$$\lim_{x\to 1^+} x^3 - 1 = 0,$$

since $f$ is continuous at 1. Hence, by the Reciprocal Rule,

$$\frac{1}{f(x)} = \frac{1}{x^3 - 1} \to \infty \text{ as } x \to 1^+.$$

**2.2** **(a)** Since

$$f(x) = \frac{2x^3 + x}{x^3} = 2 + \frac{1}{x^2}, \quad \text{for } x \neq 0,$$

we deduce, by Theorem 2.1(b) and the Sum Rule, that

$$f(x) = 2 + \frac{1}{x^2} \to 2 + 0 = 2 \text{ as } x \to \infty.$$

**(b)** Let

$$f(x) = \frac{x^2}{2x^3 + 1};$$

then $f(x) > 0$ for $x \in (0, \infty)$, and

$$f(x) = \frac{1/x}{2 + 1/x^3} \to \frac{0}{2 + 0} = 0 \text{ as } x \to \infty,$$

by Theorem 2.1(b) and the Combination Rules.

Hence, by the Reciprocal Rule,

$$\frac{1}{f(x)} = \frac{2x^3 + 1}{x^2} \to \infty \text{ as } x \to \infty.$$

**2.3** Since $-1 \le \sin(1/x) \le 1$ for $x \neq 0$, we have

$$-\frac{1}{x} \le \frac{\sin(1/x)}{x} \le \frac{1}{x}, \quad \text{for } x \in (0, \infty).$$

Also, by Theorem 2.1(b) and the Multiple Rule,

$$g(x) = -\frac{1}{x} \to 0 \text{ as } x \to \infty$$

and

$$h(x) = \frac{1}{x} \to 0 \text{ as } x \to \infty.$$

Thus, by the Squeeze Rule, part (a),

$$f(x) = \frac{\sin(1/x)}{x} \to 0 \text{ as } x \to \infty.$$

**2.4** (a) By Theorem 2.2(b), we have

$$\frac{e^x}{x^2} \to \infty \text{ as } x \to \infty.$$

By Theorem 2.2(c), we have

$$\frac{\log_e x}{x^2} \to 0 \text{ as } x \to \infty.$$

Also, $(\log_e x)/x^2 > 0$ for $x > 1$, so

$$\frac{x^2}{\log_e x} \to \infty \text{ as } x \to \infty,$$

by the Reciprocal Rule.

Hence, by the Combination Rules,

$$\frac{e^x}{x^2} + \frac{3x^2}{\log_e x} \to \infty \text{ as } x \to \infty.$$

(b) Following the hint, we write

$$\frac{\log_e x}{e^x} = \left(\frac{\log_e x}{x}\right)\left(\frac{x}{e^x}\right).$$

By Theorem 2.2(b) and (c),

$$\frac{x}{e^x} \to 0 \text{ as } x \to \infty \quad \text{and} \quad \frac{\log_e x}{x} \to 0 \text{ as } x \to \infty.$$

Thus, by the Product Rule,

$$\frac{\log_e x}{e^x} \to 0 \times 0 = 0 \text{ as } x \to \infty.$$

(c) The dominant term is $e^x$, so we write

$$\frac{2e^x - x^2}{e^x + \log_e x} = \frac{2 - x^2/e^x}{1 + (\log_e x)/e^x}.$$

Thus, by part (b) above, Theorem 2.2(b) and the Combination Rules,

$$\frac{2e^x - x^2}{e^x + \log_e x} \to \frac{2-0}{1+0} = 2 \text{ as } x \to \infty.$$

**2.5** (a) We can write

$$\frac{e^{x^2}}{x^2} = g(f(x)),$$

where $f(x) = x^2$ and $g(x) = e^x/x$.

Substituting $u = f(x) = x^2$, we have (by Theorem 2.2(a) and (b))

$$u = x^2 \to \infty \text{ as } x \to \infty,$$

$$g(u) = \frac{e^u}{u} \to \infty \text{ as } u \to \infty.$$

Thus, by the Composition Rule,

$$g(f(x)) = \frac{e^{x^2}}{x^2} \to \infty \text{ as } x \to \infty.$$

(b) We can write

$$\log_e(\log_e x) = g(f(x)),$$

where $f(x) = \log_e x$ and $g(x) = \log_e x$.

Substituting $u = f(x) = \log_e x$, we have (by Theorem 2.2(c))

$$u = \log_e x \to \infty \text{ as } x \to \infty,$$

$$g(u) = \log_e u \to \infty \text{ as } u \to \infty.$$

Thus, by the Composition Rule,

$$g(f(x)) = \log_e(\log_e x) \to \infty \text{ as } x \to \infty.$$

(c) We can write

$$x\sin(1/x) = \frac{\sin(1/x)}{1/x} = g(f(x)),$$

where $f(x) = \dfrac{1}{x}$ and $g(u) = \dfrac{\sin u}{u}$.

Substituting $u = f(x) = 1/x$, we have

$$u = 1/x \to 0 \text{ as } x \to \infty \quad \text{(Theorem 2.1(b))},$$

$$g(u) = \frac{\sin u}{u} \to 1 \text{ as } u \to 0 \quad \text{(Theorem 1.1)}.$$

Thus, by the Composition Rule,

$$g(f(x)) = x\sin(1/x) \to 1 \text{ as } x \to \infty.$$

**2.6** (a) Let $f(x) = x^4$; then $f(x) > 0$ for $x \in \mathbb{R} - \{0\}$, and

$$\lim_{x \to 0} x^4 = 0,$$

since $f$ is continuous at 0.

Hence, by the Reciprocal Rule,

$$\frac{1}{f(x)} = \frac{1}{x^4} \to \infty \text{ as } x \to 0.$$

(b) Let

$$f(x) = \frac{1}{\cot x} = \tan x;$$

then

$$f(x) > 0, \quad \text{for } 0 < x < \pi/2,$$

and $f$ is continuous on $(-\frac{1}{2}\pi, \frac{1}{2}\pi)$ with $f(0) = 0$, so

$$f(x) \to 0 \text{ as } x \to 0^+.$$

Hence, by the Reciprocal Rule,

$$\frac{1}{f(x)} = \cot x \to \infty \text{ as } x \to 0^+.$$

(c) Let

$$f(x) = \frac{1}{e^x - x};$$

then

$$f(x) > 0, \quad \text{for } x > 0,$$

since $e^x > 1 + x$ for $x > 0$, and

$$f(x) = \frac{1/e^x}{1 - x/e^x} \to \frac{0}{1-0} = 0 \text{ as } x \to \infty,$$

by Theorem 2.2(b) and the Combination Rules.

Hence, by the Reciprocal Rule,

$$\frac{1}{f(x)} = e^x - x \to \infty \text{ as } x \to \infty.$$

(Alternatively, since $e^x = 1 + x + x^2/2! + \cdots$, for $x > 0$, we have

$$e^x - x > x^2/2, \quad \text{for } x > 0,$$

so

$$e^x - x \to \infty \text{ as } x \to \infty,$$

by Theorem 2.1(a) and part (b) of the Squeeze Rule.)

**(d)** We can write

$$\log_e x = -\log_e(1/x) = g(f(x)),$$

where $f(x) = 1/x$ and $g(u) = -\log_e u$.

Substituting $u = f(x) = 1/x$, we have

$$u = 1/x \to \infty \text{ as } x \to 0^+ \text{ (Reciprocal Rule)},$$

$$g(u) = -\log_e u \to -\infty \text{ as } u \to \infty,$$

by Theorem 2.2(c).

Thus, by the Composition Rule,

$$g(f(x)) = \log_e x \to -\infty \text{ as } x \to 0^+.$$

**(e)** Since

$$-1 \leq \sin x \leq 1, \quad \text{for } x \in \mathbb{R},$$

we have

$$x + \sin x \geq x - 1, \quad \text{for } x \in \mathbb{R}.$$

By Theorem 2.2(a), we have

$$x - 1 \to \infty \text{ as } x \to \infty,$$

so, by part (b) of the Squeeze Rule,

$$x + \sin x \to \infty \text{ as } x \to \infty.$$

**(f)** First note that for $x > 0$,

$$x^x = \exp(x \log_e x) = g(f(x)),$$

where $f(x) = x \log_e x$ and $g(x) = \exp(x)$.

Substituting $u = x \log_e x$, we have

$$u = x \log_e x \to \infty \text{ as } x \to \infty,$$

by Theorem 2.2(c) and the Product Rule, and

$$\exp(u) = e^u \to \infty \text{ as } u \to \infty,$$

by Theorem 2.2(b). Thus, by the Composition Rule,

$$g(f(x)) = x^x \to \infty \text{ as } x \to \infty.$$

(Alternatively, for $x \geq e$ we have

$$x^x \geq e^x,$$

so we can deduce the result from part (b) of the Squeeze Rule and Theorem 2.2(b).)

**(g)** First note that for $x > 0$,

$$x^{1/x} = \exp\left(\frac{1}{x} \log_e x\right) = g(f(x)),$$

where $f(x) = (\log_e x)/x$ and $g(x) = \exp(x)$.

Substituting $u = (\log_e x)/x$, we have

$$u = (\log_e x)/x \to 0 \text{ as } x \to \infty,$$

by Theorem 2.2(c), and

$$\exp(u) = e^u \to 1 \text{ as } u \to 0,$$

since $g$ is continuous on 0. Thus, by the Composition Rule,

$$g(f(x)) = x^{1/x} \to 1 \text{ as } x \to \infty.$$

**(h)** We have

$$\frac{x^2 + \log_e x}{x + e^x} = \frac{x^2/e^x + (\log_e x)/e^x}{x/e^x + 1}.$$

Thus, by the solution to Exercise 2.4(b), Theorem 2.2(b) and the Combination Rules,

$$\frac{x^2 + \log_e x}{x + e^x} \to \frac{0 + 0}{0 + 1} = 0 \text{ as } x \to \infty.$$

**3.1** The domain of $f(x) = x^3$ is $\mathbb{R}$.

Let $\varepsilon > 0$ be given. We want to choose $\delta > 0$, in terms of $\varepsilon$, such that

$$|f(x) - f(1)| < \varepsilon, \quad \text{for all } x \text{ with } |x - 1| < \delta. \quad \text{(S.1)}$$

1. First we write
$$f(x) - f(1) = x^3 - 1 = (x - 1)(x^2 + x + 1).$$
2. Next we obtain an upper bound for $|x^2 + x + 1|$ when $x$ is near 1. If $|x - 1| \leq 1$, then $x$ lies in the interval $[0, 2]$, so (by the Triangle Inequality)
$$|x^2 + x + 1| \leq |x|^2 + |x| + 1 \leq 2^2 + 2 + 1 = 7.$$
3. Hence
$$|f(x) - f(1)| \leq 7|x - 1|, \quad \text{for } |x - 1| \leq 1.$$
So if $|x - 1| < \delta$, where $0 < \delta \leq 1$, then
$$|f(x) - f(1)| < 7\delta.$$
Thus, if we choose $\delta = \min\{1, \tfrac{1}{7}\varepsilon\}$, then
$$|f(x) - f(1)| < 7\delta \leq \varepsilon, \text{ for all } x \text{ with } |x - 1| < \delta,$$
which proves statement (S.1).

Thus $f$ is continuous at the point 1.

**3.2** The domain of

$$f(x) = \frac{2x^3 + 3x - 5}{x - 1}$$

is $\mathbb{R} - \{1\}$, so $f$ is defined on each punctured neighbourhood of 1. Also, for $x \neq 1$,

$$f(x) = \frac{2x^3 + 3x - 5}{x - 1} = \frac{(x - 1)(2x^2 + 2x + 5)}{(x - 1)} = 2x^2 + 2x + 5.$$

This suggests that

$$\lim_{x \to 1} f(x) = 2 \times 1^2 + 2 \times 1 + 5 = 9,$$

so we must prove that

for each $\varepsilon > 0$, there exists $\delta > 0$ such that
$$|f(x) - 9| < \varepsilon, \text{ for all } x \text{ with } 0 < |x - 1| < \delta. \quad \text{(S.2)}$$

1. First we write, for $x \neq 1$,
$$f(x) - 9 = 2x^2 + 2x + 5 - 9 = 2(x^2 + x - 2) = 2(x - 1)(x + 2).$$
2. Next, if $|x - 1| \leq 1$, then $x$ lies in the interval $[0, 2]$, so (by the Triangle Inequality)
$$|2(x + 2)| \leq 2(|x| + 2) \leq 2(2 + 2) = 8.$$

3. Hence

$$|f(x) - 9| \le 8|x-1|, \quad \text{for } 0 < |x-1| \le 1.$$

So if $0 < |x-1| < \delta$, where $0 < \delta \le 1$, then

$$|f(x) - 9| < 8\delta.$$

Thus, if we choose $\delta = \min\{1, \frac{1}{8}\varepsilon\}$, then

$$|f(x) - 9| < 8\delta \le \varepsilon, \text{ for all } x \text{ with } 0 < |x-1| < \delta,$$

which proves statement (S.2).

Hence

$$\lim_{x\to 1} f(x) = 9.$$

**3.3** **(a)** The domain of $f(x) = 6x^2 - x$ is $\mathbb{R}$.

Let $\varepsilon > 0$ be given. We want to choose $\delta > 0$, in terms of $\varepsilon$, such that

$$|f(x) - f(-1)| < \varepsilon, \text{ for all } x \text{ with } |x+1| < \delta. \quad \text{(S.3)}$$

1. First we write

$$f(x) - f(-1) = 6x^2 - x - 7 = (x+1)(6x-7).$$

2. Next we obtain an upper bound for $|6x-7|$ when $x$ is near $-1$. If $|x+1| \le 1$, then $x$ lies in the interval $[-2, 0]$, so (by the Triangle Inequality)

$$\begin{aligned}|6x-7| &\le |6x| + |-7| = 6|x| + 7\\ &\le 6 \times 2 + 7 = 19.\end{aligned}$$

3. Hence

$$|f(x) - f(-1)| \le 19|x+1|, \quad \text{for } |x+1| \le 1.$$

So if $|x+1| < \delta$, where $0 < \delta \le 1$, then

$$|f(x) - f(-1)| < 19\delta.$$

Thus, if we choose $\delta = \min\{1, \frac{1}{19}\varepsilon\}$, then

$$|f(x) - f(-1)| < 19\delta \le \varepsilon,$$
for all $x$ with $|x+1| < \delta$,

which proves statement (S.3).

Thus $f$ is continuous at the point $-1$.

**(b)** The domain of $f(x) = x^5$ is $\mathbb{R}$.

Let $\varepsilon > 0$ be given. We want to choose $\delta > 0$, in terms of $\varepsilon$, such that

$$|f(x) - f(0)| < \varepsilon, \quad \text{for all } x \text{ with } |x| < \delta. \quad \text{(S.4)}$$

In this case it is possible to use Strategy 3.1, but it is easier to note that

$$|f(x) - f(0)| < \varepsilon \quad \text{is equivalent to} \quad |x|^5 < \varepsilon.$$

Thus, if we choose $\delta = \sqrt[5]{\varepsilon}$, then

$$|f(x) - f(0)| = |x|^5 < \delta^5 = \varepsilon, \text{ for all } x \text{ with } |x| < \delta,$$

which proves statement (S.4).

Thus $f$ is continuous at the point 0.

**(c)** The domain of $f(x) = \sqrt{x}$ is $[0, \infty)$.

Let $\varepsilon > 0$ be given. We want to choose $\delta > 0$, in terms of $\varepsilon$, such that

$$|f(x) - f(4)| < \varepsilon, \text{ for all } x \text{ with } |x-4| < \delta. \quad \text{(S.5)}$$

1. First we use the hint to write

$$f(x) - f(4) = \sqrt{x} - 2 = \frac{x-4}{\sqrt{x}+2}.$$

2. Next we obtain an upper bound for

$$\left|\frac{1}{\sqrt{x}+2}\right|$$

when $x$ is near 4. If $|x-4| \le 1$, then $x$ lies in the interval $[3, 5]$, so $\sqrt{x} + 2 \ge \sqrt{3} + 2$, and thus

$$\left|\frac{1}{\sqrt{x}+2}\right| \le \frac{1}{\sqrt{3}+2} \le 1.$$

3. Hence

$$|f(x) - f(4)| \le |x-4|, \quad \text{for } |x-4| \le 1.$$

So if $|x-4| < \delta$, where $0 < \delta \le 1$, then

$$|f(x) - f(4)| < \delta.$$

Thus, if we choose $\delta = \min\{1, \varepsilon\}$, then

$$|f(x) - f(4)| < \delta \le \varepsilon,$$
for all $x$ with $|x-4| < \delta$,

which proves statement (S.5).

Thus $f$ is continuous at the point 4.

**(d)** The domain of $f(x) = 1/x$ is $\mathbb{R} - \{0\}$.

Let $\varepsilon > 0$ be given. We want to choose $\delta > 0$, in terms of $\varepsilon$, such that

$$|f(x) - f(1)| < \varepsilon, \quad \text{for all } x \text{ with } |x-1| < \delta. \quad \text{(S.6)}$$

1. First we write

$$f(x) - f(1) = \frac{1}{x} - 1 = \frac{1-x}{x} = (x-1)\left(\frac{-1}{x}\right).$$

2. Next we obtain an upper bound for $|-1/x|$ when $x$ is near 1. If $|x-1| \le \frac{1}{2}$ (chosen to avoid the point 0), then $x$ lies in the interval $[\frac{1}{2}, \frac{3}{2}]$, so $x \ge \frac{1}{2}$ and hence

$$\left|\frac{-1}{x}\right| = \frac{1}{x} \le 2.$$

3. Hence

$$|f(x) - f(1)| \le 2|x-1|, \quad \text{for } |x-1| \le \tfrac{1}{2}.$$

So if $|x-1| < \delta$, where $0 < \delta \le \frac{1}{2}$, then

$$|f(x) - f(1)| < 2\delta.$$

Thus, if we choose $\delta = \min\{\frac{1}{2}, \frac{1}{2}\varepsilon\}$, then

$$|f(x) - f(1)| < 2\delta \le \varepsilon,$$
for all $x$ with $|x-1| < \delta$,

which proves statement (S.6).

Thus $f$ is continuous at the point 1.

**3.4** The domain of

$$f(x) = \frac{x^3+1}{x+1}$$

is $\mathbb{R} - \{-1\}$, so $f$ is defined on each punctured neighbourhood of $-1$. Also, for $x \ne -1$,

$$\begin{aligned}f(x) = \frac{x^3+1}{x+1} &= \frac{(x+1)(x^2-x+1)}{x+1}\\ &= x^2 - x + 1.\end{aligned}$$

This suggests that

$$\lim_{x\to -1} f(x) = (-1)^2 - (-1) + 1 = 3,$$

so we must prove that

for each $\varepsilon > 0$, there exists $\delta > 0$ such that
$|f(x) - 3| < \varepsilon$, for all $x$ with $0 < |x+1| < \delta$. (S.7)

1. First we write, for $x \neq -1$,
$$f(x) - 3 = x^2 - x + 1 - 3 = x^2 - x - 2 = (x+1)(x-2).$$
2. Next, if $|x+1| \leq 1$, then $x$ lies in the interval $[-2, 0]$, so (by the Triangle Inequality)
$$|x-2| \leq |x| + 2 \leq 2 + 2 = 4.$$
3. Hence
$$|f(x) - 3| \leq 4|x+1|, \quad \text{for } 0 < |x+1| \leq 1.$$
So if $0 < |x+1| < \delta$, where $0 < \delta \leq 1$, then
$$|f(x) - 3| < 4\delta.$$
Thus if we choose $\delta = \min\{1, \frac{1}{4}\varepsilon\}$, then
$$|f(x) - 3| < 4\delta \leq \varepsilon, \text{ for all } x \text{ with } 0 < |x+1| < \delta,$$
which proves statement (S.7).

Hence
$$\lim_{x \to -1} f(x) = 3.$$

**4.1** **(a)** We use Strategy 4.1, part 1. Let $\varepsilon > 0$ be given. We have
$$f(x) - f(y) = x^3 - y^3 = (x-y)(x^2 + xy + y^2),$$
so for $x, y \in [-2, 2]$ (by the Triangle Inequality),
$$|f(x) - f(y)| = |x-y|\,|x^2 + xy + y^2| \leq (|x|^2 + |x|\,|y| + |y|^2)|x-y| \leq 12|x-y|,$$
since $|x| \leq 2$ and $|y| \leq 2$.

Thus, if we choose $\delta = \frac{1}{12}\varepsilon$, then whenever $x, y \in [-2, 2]$ and $|x-y| < \delta$, we have
$$|f(x) - f(y)| \leq 12|x-y| < 12 \times \tfrac{1}{12}\varepsilon = \varepsilon.$$
Hence $f$ is uniformly continuous on $[-2, 2]$.

**(b)** Following Strategy 4.1, part 2, and the hint, we take $x_n = n + 1/n$ and $y_n = n$, $n = 1, 2, \ldots$. Both sequences lie in $I = \mathbb{R}$ and
$$|x_n - y_n| = (n + 1/n) - n = 1/n \to 0 \text{ as } n \to \infty,$$
$$|f(x_n) - f(y_n)| = |x_n^2 - y_n^2| = (n + 1/n)^2 - n^2 = n^2 + 2n(1/n) + (1/n)^2 - n^2 = 2 + 1/n^2 \geq 2, \quad \text{for } n = 1, 2, \ldots.$$
Thus, by taking $\varepsilon = 2$ in Strategy 4.1, part 2, we deduce that $f$ is not uniformly continuous on $\mathbb{R}$.

**4.2** Since $f(x) = x^3$ is continuous on its domain $\mathbb{R}$, we deduce that $f$ is continuous on the bounded closed interval $[-2, 2]$. Thus $f$ is uniformly continuous on $[-2, 2]$, by Theorem 4.2.

**4.3** **(a)** Let $\varepsilon > 0$ be given. For $x, y \in \mathbb{R}$, we have
$$f(x) - f(y) = x - y,$$
so
$$|f(x) - f(y)| = |x - y|.$$
Thus, if we choose $\delta = \varepsilon$, then whenever $x, y \in \mathbb{R}$ and $|x - y| < \delta$, we have
$$|f(x) - f(y)| = |x - y| < \delta = \varepsilon.$$
Hence $f$ is uniformly continuous on $\mathbb{R}$.

**(b)** Following Strategy 4.1, part 2, we take $x_n = 1/(2n)$ and $y_n = 1/n$, $n = 1, 2, \ldots$. Both sequences lie in $I = (0, 3]$ and
$$|x_n - y_n| = \left|\frac{1}{2n} - \frac{1}{n}\right| = \frac{1}{2n} \to 0 \text{ as } n \to \infty,$$
$$|f(x_n) - f(y_n)| = \left|\frac{1}{x_n^2} - \frac{1}{y_n^2}\right| = \left|\frac{1}{(1/(2n))^2} - \frac{1}{(1/n)^2}\right| = 4n^2 - n^2 = 3n^2 \geq 3, \quad \text{for } n = 1, 2, \ldots.$$
Thus, by taking $\varepsilon = 3$ in Strategy 4.1, part 2, we deduce that $f$ is not uniformly continuous on $(0, 3]$.

**(c)** Let $\varepsilon > 0$ be given. For $x, y \in [0, \infty)$, we have
$$f(x) - f(y) = \frac{2x}{1+x} - \frac{2y}{1+y} = \frac{2(x-y)}{(1+x)(1+y)}.$$
Since $1 + x \geq 1$ and $1 + y \geq 1$, for $x, y \in [0, \infty)$,
$$|f(x) - f(y)| \leq 2|x - y|, \quad \text{for } x, y \in [0, \infty).$$
Thus, if we choose $\delta = \frac{1}{2}\varepsilon$, then whenever $x, y \in [0, \infty)$ and $|x - y| < \delta$, we have
$$|f(x) - f(y)| \leq 2|x - y| < 2\delta = \varepsilon.$$
Hence $f$ is uniformly continuous on $[0, \infty)$.

**(d)** Following Strategy 4.1, part 2, we take $x_n = n + 1/n$ and $y_n = n$, $n = 1, 2, \ldots$. Both sequences lie in $I = \mathbb{R}$ and
$$|x_n - y_n| = (n + 1/n) - n = 1/n \to 0 \text{ as } n \to \infty,$$
$$|f(x_n) - f(y_n)| = |e^{x_n} - e^{y_n}| = e^{n+1/n} - e^n = e^n(e^{1/n} - 1) \geq n \times (1/n) = 1, \quad \text{for } n = 1, 2, \ldots,$$
by using the inequality $e^x \geq 1 + x \geq x$, for $x \geq 0$.

Thus, by taking $\varepsilon = 1$ in Strategy 4.1, part 2, we deduce that $f$ is not uniformly continuous on $\mathbb{R}$.

**4.4** Since $f(x) = 2x/(1+x)$ is a rational function, it is continuous on its domain $\mathbb{R} - \{-1\}$ and hence on the bounded closed interval $[-\frac{1}{2}, 0]$. We deduce that $f$ is uniformly continuous on $[-\frac{1}{2}, 0]$, by Theorem 4.2.

# Index